EnGr

The
New
Electronics

McGRAW-HILL SERIES
IN CONTINUING EDUCATION
FOR ENGINEERS

Florman ENGINEERING AND THE LIBERAL ARTS

Hodge COMPUTERS FOR ENGINEERS

Shore THE NEW ELECTRONICS

BRUCE H. SHORE
Science Editor, RCA Corporation

The
New
Electronics

New York   St. Louis   McGRAW-HILL BOOK COMPANY

San Francisco   London   Sydney   Toronto   Mexico   Panama

THE NEW ELECTRONICS

Library of Congress Catalog Card Number 78–81612

57042

1234567890   MAMM   7543210

Foreword

The development of the point-contact transistor in 1948 marked the beginning of a profound change in the nature and practice of electronics both as a science and as an industry. Before this time, starting with the discovery of the electron by J. J. Thomson in 1897 and the invention of the *audion* by Lee DeForest in 1907, electronics was an activity concerned with the study, control, and application of electrons released into vacuum. After that date, it became an activity concerned primarily with the study, control, and application of electrons confined in the solid state.

During its first, or vacuum, period, roughly fifty years in

duration, electronics led to some of man's most impressive achievements—radio, sound motion pictures, television, the electron microscope, microwave radar, and the computer. During the second, or solid-state, period from 1948 to the present, it has added to this notable list the achievements of the transistor, the tunnel diode, the silicon controlled rectifier, the integrated circuit, the laser, the superconductive magnet, and holography. Still more is expected.

In the course of the past seven years, as administrator of scientific information for RCA Laboratories in Princeton, New Jersey, and on the RCA corporate staff in New York City I have had a unique coign of vantage from which to observe the rapid evolution of this second phase, even as I have been able to live with and study the technological fruits and manifestations of the first phase. Thus, although the emphasis of this book is on solid-state electronics, I have been at pains to review its development naturally from the pioneering experiments, investigations, theories, and hardware of vacuum electronics. Moreover, wherever practicable, I have included names, dates, and historical information on both phases in order to reinforce the text and to afford reference points for the benefit of the more demanding or more sophisticated reader who wishes to find deeper treatments of the subjects discussed.

Finally, because modern solid-state electronics is so divorced from everyday experience with its heavy dependence on quantum-mechanical theory and such mathematical hermetica as Bose-Einstein and Fermi-Dirac statistics, I have resorted to a frankly literary style in the text. This has been done to assure that the widest possible audience may read it with both enjoyment and profit.

Bruce H. Shore

Acknowledgments

"No man is an island unto himself," says the poet, and nowhere is this more apparent than in the writing of a book.
It is no act of modesty then to cite several associates—especially the individual scientists and engineers making up the
corps de recherche of RCA Laboratories—for their generous and
interested help in bringing this project to a successful conclusion. In that connection, I should like to single out for
special mention Drs. Albert Rose, Dwight North, Henry
Lewis, Karl Zaininger, and Steven Hofstein for consistent and
invaluable aid on the scientific aspects of the text; R. Kenyon
Kilbon and Chester W. Sall for editorial advice and steadfast

encouragement; Miss Phyllis Smith and Mrs. Zenith Gross for library search activities and bibliographical assistance; and, finally, Norman Newell and Thomas Cook for the exquisite photography supporting the text. A special thanks, also, to Jules Koslow, editor of the RCA magazine, *Electronic Age,* in which the bulk of the material composing the chapters of this book has appeared over the past few years.

Bruce H. Shore

Contents

The
New
Electronics

Dr. Albert Rose is caught in intense discussion with a young colleague (off camera) who has sought his guidance.

CHAPTER 1

The
Research
Theorist

Theory is the poetry of mathematics, and, like poetry, its essence is metaphor—the sudden equation of separate ideas that elucidates, systematizes, and unites them for the first time.

"All the world's a stage," cries the poet.

"$E = mc^2$," exclaims the theorist.

Both statements are metaphors, in their own language, and both equate hitherto unrelated concepts in new and powerful ways, affording fresh insight into their nature and a deepened understanding of their meaning.

Mathematics is a language, in much the same way that English is a language. It has subjects, objects, predicates, modi-

Scientist inserts metal rod whose top holds a tiny, Gunn effect oscillator into a microwave cavity where it will be used to generate watts of high-frequency microwave power in an experimental communications system.

fiers, and syntax. Its nouns are numbers, and its verbs are *add, subtract, multiply, divide,* and *equals*—its chief verb, *to be.*

Still, it is a peculiar sort of language. It always speaks in the third person and always in the present tense. Its nouns have the stark, indisputable meaning of number, and its sentences are equations that describe the interdependence of these numerical nouns and nothing more.

Herein lies its secret, however. For, an interdependent relationship, whether of people or things, is one of cause and effect—a principle considered basic to the structure of every event in nature from the formation of a galaxy to the fission of an atom. Thus, mathematics is a language designed to express cause and effect either abstractly, in a context of pure numbers, or concretely, in a context of natural phenomena whose values have been numerically coded. In the first case, it is the idiom of the mathematician; in the second, of the scientist.

There are many kinds of scientists, however, and they use this language in many different ways. What distinguishes the theorist among them is his use of mathematics not only to describe cause and effect in nature but to discover it. He uses his language like a poet, not merely to register but to relate his observations and, by so doing, to explain them. Like the poet, he depends upon insight and linguistic invention, upon metaphor and figures of speech, upon form and meter. The principal difference is that his medium is mathematics, his metaphors are equations, and his meter is the universal rhythm of nature.

There is one more difference. The truth of a poet's insight can never be finally shown. It is valid subjectively, only as we think it is. Not so the insight of the theorist. Theory must be objective. It must be able to explain events and to predict them, not only for this generation but for all generations. It is poetic, yes. But it is more than poetry.

The theorist's fluency in mathematics, coupled with his poetic power to fashion from it valid metaphors that unite matter and energy, time and space in original and compelling ways, has won for him, recently, a numerically small but vital role in American industry. This is especially so in electronics, where the need for theorists became acute following the introduction of the transistor in 1948.

Here was a device that could switch, amplify, or modulate an electric current passing through it just as a vacuum tube could. There was one momentous difference, however. Whereas the tube was a precise assembly of separate parts—cathode, grid, anode—mounted in a glass-enclosed vacuum, the transistor was a single chunk of solid germanium no bigger than a grain of sand. (Later on, with the introduction of the silicon transistor in the mid-1950s, it quite literally became a product of sand—man-made, of course.)

The significance of this unexpected development was that the electronics manufacturer, like the United States government before him, found himself catapulted abruptly into his own version of the atomic age. His next generation of components could not be assembled from mechanical parts. It would have to be synthesized from raw atoms.

But, what atoms? What were the laws governing their behavior? How did electrons act in such a strange environment, and how did one condition this environment to produce useful electronic phenomena?

These were tough questions with important business overtones, and there were no ready answers inside the electronics industry. What was needed was someone who understood solid-state theory and knew how to apply it. The only man fitting this description was the solid-state theorist.

Fortunately, the electronics industry was not caught totally unprepared. It had been conducting solid-state research of some kind for more than two decades. For instance, two years prior to the announcement of the transistor, several industrial research groups had sought to learn why the current flow through the oxide surface of the cathode in a vacuum tube started out large and then dwindled to a small though steady trickle. It was certainly an obscure investigation, but one which gave unexpected insight into the fundamentals of electron conduction in semiconductors—the basis of the transistor.

Because of such pioneering investigations, the electronics industry was able to act immediately when Dr. William Shockley, a member of the Bell Telephone Laboratories team that developed the transistor, published his definitive book on the subject in 1950. Shortly thereafter, the industry moved from theory to practice, and by 1952 it was producing germanium transistors for hearing aids and pocket radios as a starter.

Again, as with the achievement of controlled nuclear fission in 1942, the theorist had proved his economic worth. His equations and formulas, his theorems and proofs were not just abstract exercises. They had profound bearing on the real world and could be used to afford man an elemental mastery over nature. American industry was impressed, and in the personnel files of many large companies, "theorist" began to crop up as a job classification alongside such venerable titles as "engineer," "chemist," and "physicist."

Why had it taken industry so long to appreciate the power of theory to strengthen its going product lines and lay the foundation for those of the future? At least three answers must be given.

First, the body of physical theory which has now made it possible for man to split the atom, harness the electron, and ride the electromagnetic wave did not even exist a generation ago. Its compilation began in 1873 with publication by James Clerk Maxwell of his theory on the electromagnetic nature of light and was consummated in 1925 with publication of

Dr. Dwight O. North is absorbed in calculations relating to acoustoelectric effects. A wealth of unread periodicals is stacked to his right.

Dr. Murray Lampert works on several new equations he is developing to help explain the behavior of electrons in insulators. In the foreground is a Greek head picked up on one of his trips to Greece.

Erwin Schrödinger's epochal wave equation relating the wave and particle properties of matter.

In between came the profound contributions of such gifted men as Ludwig Boltzmann, Josiah Willard Gibbs, Max Planck, Albert Einstein, Niels Bohr, Werner Heisenberg, and Louis de Broglie. As a body, these were the men who comprised the Constitutional Convention of modern physics, who wrote the laws and framed the articles by which we are still bound in our relations to physical reality. Interestingly, all of them wrote in cogent metaphor:

> . . . light is electricity and magnetism
>
> . . . heat is atomic motion
>
> . . . mass is energy
>
> . . . gravity is acceleration
>
> . . . matter is both particle and wave

The second reason for industry's delay in hiring the theorist lay in the character of the theorist himself. He was and is a loner, a man inured to privacy and the quiet monasticism of thought. His instinct, his background, his training—all combine to direct him toward a position in the physics department of a university. Thus, he was ill-disposed to enter the pragmatic hurly-burly that marks commercial life.

Finally, there was industry itself. It was and is a doer. Design products, get into production, cut costs, raise profits, beat the competition—that's the ticket! If a new product is needed, invent it. If one material fails to work, use another. In such a milieu, it was hard to see the worth of paying a man just to sit there and think!

By the end of World War II, however, all this had begun to change. The practical power of theory had been demonstrated at Alamogordo, New Mexico, and the theorist had begun to see that his numerical metaphors could have social, political, and economic meaning.

The industrialist, too, had begun to change. The war effort had pushed him to the limit of his existing technologies into a regime in materials and phenomena beyond his competence. At this juncture, in the electronics industry specifically, the transistor materialized and, on its heels, the digital computer.

In the case of the transistor, the need for theorists was immediate and obvious. In the case of the computer, it was less so, at first. Was not computer manufacture simply an assembling of parts, a procedure that industry already knew well?

It was, indeed, but it was more than that. The computer was potentially capable of solving just about any problem that could be reduced to the language of mathematics, from the orbital velocity of space satellites to the production bottlenecks of industry. It could have a kind of mental life all its own, if one but knew how to program for it.

What was needed were not physical theorists but design theorists skilled in the morphologic rigors of information processing. Fortunately, the world's universities had been producing such wizards—steeped in the lore of symbolic logic, propositional calculus, combinatorics, the theory of sets, and the theory of probability—since about 1940. They were there, and industry hurried to enlist them. Today, they are behind the computer's growing mastery of a thousand different tasks.

Right now, for instance, in many of the nation's ranking electronics laboratories, members of this select fraternity are leading crack teams of information-processing theorists across a no-man's-land of switching networks and stored programs toward such astonishing goals as machines that adapt to changing situations, that read print, and that even display rudimentary intelligence.

To explore new ideas, to create new metaphors that bridge the discontinuities in nature, to build mathematical models of reality—these are still the paramount business of the theorist, even in industry. But with time and usage have come other

Dr. Saul Amarel puffs pensively on his pipe as he seeks to explain the nature of his work with combinatorics, symbolic logic, and the other disciplines that may one day make artificial intelligence possible.

Dr. Robert Parmenter is seen searching through a text in the library of RCA Laboratories in Princeton. Dr. Parmenter is a leading specialist in the fields of superconductivity and superfluidity.

tasks and other responsibilities. For example, the theorist is frequently asked to use his descriptive powers in mathematics to interpret, within the limits of accepted theory, the events going on in new materials or new components emerging from the materials and devices laboratories. Thus, he may divide his time between trying to solve the riddle of superconductivity per se and trying to describe the behavior of known super-conductive materials.

It is also important, in an industrial laboratory, to know the limitations of the devices and systems already developed. At the least, such knowledge prevents trying to do the impossible. At most, it delineates what performance goals can be set. This was the effect of Dr. Dwight North's classic study at RCA of the sources of noise in pulse radar systems during World War II. This paper has had worldwide circulation and is still considered to be, some twenty-five years after its composition, the basic reference for anyone wishing to build such systems.

Following the scientific literature, maintaining personal touch with key members of the scientific community, staying abreast of critical research going forward in the laboratories— these are other functions carried on by the industrial theorist, both for his own benefit and for that of his management.

Probably one of the theorist's most valuable ancillary roles, however, is as a catalyst to invention. Since he does not do experiments himself and does not synthesize materials, he must content himself with inspiring others to do so. Thus, he circulates a lot, pokes into various laboratories that interest him, buttonholes colleagues he feels can benefit from his ideas, encourages others to air their research problems with him, and in general, attempts to spark the inventive process.

Finally, there is the theorist's responsibility to advise research management on what significant scientific trends are developing, what new lines of research should be opened, where current activities should be curtailed, and so on through the thousand natural cares to which research managers are heir.

To counsel, to catalyze, to create—these are the responsibilities of the modern industrial theorist. In the final analysis, all three stem directly from his power not only to describe but to discover the secrets of nature in the metaphors of mathematics.

A cluster of cadmium-chromium-selenide crystals grown by a novel liquid phase transport technique is shown on a background of iron filings organized by a magnetic field. These crystals are unique in that they display hole-electron and spin-wave phenomena as well as other exotic effects.

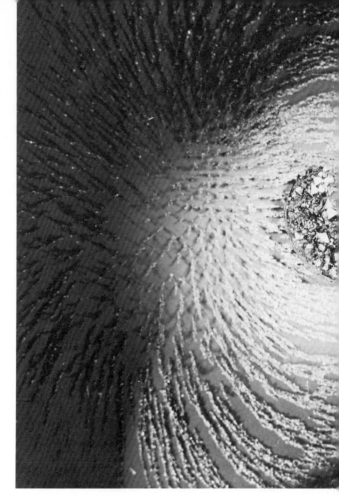

CHAPTER 2

The Quantum Caper

The negatively charged electron and the positively charged "hole" are the Adam and Eve of modern solid-state physics. Driven from their crystalline Garden of Eden by the invention of the transistor in 1948, they have been indentured by electronics scientists and engineers to work in a host of quantum devices and circuits whose number, variety, and usefulness multiply with each passing day.

Already, they have been used separately or together to realize three species of transistors for amplifying radio signals or switching electric currents around a computer (the point-contact, the junction, and the field-effect types) and at least

13

five classes of diodes for blocking and controlling alternating electric currents in a circuit or for generating high-frequency microwaves, including standard and silicon controlled rectifiers, zener diodes, tunnel diodes, and avalanche transit time diodes. In addition, they have led to several specialty items such as the solar cell for converting light directly to electricity, the semiconductive thermocouple for converting heat to electricity or electricity to cold, the "injection" or semiconductor laser for generating intense rays of coherent light directly from electric current, and the Gunn effect oscillator for generating radio waves in the millimeter spectrum above the microwave regime.

Such, so far, has been the marvelous fecundity of the hole-electron concept first introduced by the British physicist Alan Wilson in 1931 to explain how electric current is carried in a semiconductor. Emboldened by these stunning successes in converting theoretical postulates to practical power, modern solid-state physicists have now begun to rummage still more deeply in the quantum-mechanical hope chest of solid matter. As a result, they have uncovered and begun to investigate a whole new assortment of strange energy forms and quasi-particles such as excitons, double excitons, polarons, phonons, plasmons, spin and helicon waves.

Although the existence of most of these had been predicted for many years, it is only recently that some have revealed themselves in the results of highly sophisticated experiments performed on certain semimetals and semiconductors. To understand what they are and to appreciate the promise they may hold for the future of electronics, it is worthwhile to sketch briefly the picture of solid matter as physicists currently see it.

This picture began to form in 1879 when Edwin Hall, a fellow at Johns Hopkins University in Baltimore, passed an electric current through a metal strip stretched between the poles of an electromagnet. To his surprise, when the magnet was on, he found that part of the electric current was diverted to the edges of the strip at right angles to the main current as river water is diverted into an irrigation trench. He found further that he could tap this right-angle current to do work simply by attaching wires to the opposite edges of the strip.

What he had shown, in fact, was that some kind of negatively charged "fluid" was moving through the atoms of the metal to produce a flow of current. In recognition of this work, the phenomenon has since been designated the *Hall effect*.

Eight years later, in Germany, Albert von Ettingshausen and Walther Nernst performed the same experiment but used a piece of bismuth spiced with tin as their sample material. Everything went as expected with the exception of one small anomaly: the Hall current produced at the sides of the bismuth sample had a positive not a negative sign. Not surprisingly, they called what they observed the *anomalous Hall effect*.

Both experiments gave rise to much head scratching in scientific circles until 1897 when the British physicist Joseph Thomson succeeded in identifying the carrier of negative electric charge as an infinitesimal particle which has come to be called the electron. This explained Hall's results, but what had Nernst and Ettingshausen seen? Scientists shrugged. They had an even bigger problem. Where were the electrons when they were not conducting current?

In 1913, the Danish physicist Niels Bohr answered that one. They were in orbit around the atoms making up the solid, he said. Actually, of course, his answer was more subtle than that. Because of the invention of the *quantum* by Max Planck in 1900 and the brilliant use which Einstein had made of it in 1905 to explain the photoelectric effect, Bohr had to postulate an atom with many orbits in order to accommodate the many electrons of differing energies needed to cancel the positive charges (protons) lodged in the atomic nucleus. Only in this way could atoms be rendered stable and electrically neutral, as we usually find them in nature. Furthermore, he said, no electrons could exist between these orbits (now called shells) because they could never have energies that were fractions of a quantum.

The quantum, according to Planck and Einstein, is the smallest unit of energy that can exist in any given form, though there may be size differences between forms. Thus, a particle may acquire one quantum of energy or many quanta, but never half a quantum or a quantum and a half. The situation is reminiscent of the distinction made between grades of gravel. There is a unit size for each grade—fine, coarse, stony, and the like—and obvious size differences between grades, but none within grades. The concept leads inevitably to the conclusion that the universe and all its wonders could not have been carved or poured. They are the handiwork of a quantum stonemason.

With the promulgation of Bohr's theory of atomic structure, it was now possible for scientists to work out the architecture of solid matter. It must consist of crowds of atoms linked arm-in-electron-arm at their outermost orbits in almost uncountable numbers. The fact that such crowds would tend to form into striking, symmetrical patterns, like swimmers in an aquatic ballet, was also duly noted and helped explain the existence of crystals. But Bohr's model explained little else. Why these crystals had certain optical and thermal properties, why some were electrical insulators while others were electrical conductors or semiconductors, remained a mystery.

Great light was shed on all these puzzles in 1925, however, when Wolfgang Pauli, in Germany, enunciated his famous *exclusion principle,* which embodies the surprising idea that no two electrons anywhere in an atom, or aggregation of atoms, can occupy the same energy state at the same time. Here, at last, was a rule which helped explain not only why atoms have orbits, but why these orbits contain certain fixed numbers of electrons and, as a consequence, produce certain unique properties in substances made up of them.

Then, in the period between 1925 and 1930, three theoretical physicists—Werner Heisenberg, Erwin Schrödinger, and Paul Dirac—invented a new form of mathematics called *quantum mechanics* and, with it, the basis for uniting all these findings under one mathematical umbrella. It is the essence of this mathematics that all phenomena in nature can be quantized—treated as consisting of hods of quantum gravel borne on the rounded shoulders of three-dimensional space. In its equations there is no essential difference between light and matter except the number and grade of energy quanta involved.

This seemingly perverse concept led immediately to some rather fantastic ideas, such as Dirac's audacious proposal that a positive electron should exist or Heisenberg's equally brash suggestion, made in 1931, that a positive hole, capable of carrying current in certain solids, should exist. Both men have lived to see their predictions verified, nonetheless. In fact, Heisenberg's idea not only explained what Nernst and Ettingshausen had seen some forty-four years before in their anomalous Hall experiment, but it gave Alan Wilson at Cambridge University in England the last clue he needed to fashion his now famous theory of electron-hole currents in semiconductors.

Simply put, when some electrons holding a crystal of solid matter together receive enough energy from heat, light, or some other source to break free, they begin to drift through the architecture of the crystal as dust moves through a light ray. This leaves the vacated atoms slightly positive, and though they are generally unable to recapture their escaped electrons, their slight charge is sufficient for each to pull an electron over from an adjacent atom. Thus, in effect, they transfer their electron holes from themselves to their nearest neighbors, which immediately do the same thing to their nearest neighbors, and so on. The net result is that many escaped or free electrons are left drifting around just outside the capture distance of the atoms composing the crystal, even as the atoms are stealing bound electrons from each other to give the impression of positive charges being passed among them.

Finally, when an electrical potential, or voltage, is applied at opposite ends of such a crystal, the free electrons are sucked toward the positive end while the free holes feel irresistibly drawn to the negative end. Thus, a current is made to flow whose strength is a function of the number and mobility of holes and electrons free to move in opposite directions.

Based on an observation first made by the German physicist Bernhard Gudden, in 1930, Wilson also inferred that the number of free charges in a semiconductor could be altered by incorporating certain impurity atoms directly into the crystal structure of the material. Depending on what these were, their effect could be to increase the availability of either the number of holes or the number of electrons. This would be so if the impurity atoms either were better electron thieves than the atoms natural to the crystal (in which case, they would produce holes) or would drop one of their outer electrons at the first sign of an energy quantum even more readily than the natural atoms (in which case, they would produce more free electrons).

Intrigued by the originality and elegance of these ideas, the renowned Russian physicist Boris Davydov, in 1938, set himself the task of explaining theoretically what would happen if a hole-saturated region (p type) in a semiconductor abutted on an electron-saturated region (n type) in the same crystal. After some very involved thought, he concluded that an electric field would be formed inside the crystal precisely at the junction of the two regions and would be of opposite polarity to the free charges. This would prevent the charges from

Dr. George Swartz holds a wafer of indium antimonide in a pair of tweezers just above an electromagnet. When held in the center of the magnet between the cone-shaped insulators, radio waves can be propagated through it by means of helicon waves induced in the hole-electron plasma within.

Dr. Henig Phillipsborn holds several beautifully faceted cadmium-chromium-selenide crystals on a spatula for visual inspection. He is responsible for the technique which has made it possible to grow these crystals.

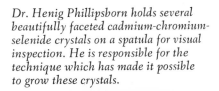

moving over into each other's domain, under normal circumstances, even though there would be an electrical attraction between them. Unfortunately for Davydov, he did not go on to ask himself what would happen if two such junctions existed in the crystal. Had he done so, we might have had the transistor ten years earlier than we did. As things stood, it was not until 1949, one year after the announcement of the point-contact transistor by John Bardeen and Walter Brattain at Bell Telephone Laboratories in Murray Hill, New Jersey, that William Shockley, also of Bell, thought to ask and answer this crucial question. The result was the invention of the junction transistor—the standard transistor of today.

The impact of the transistor on society—on communications, on military and industrial technology, on information handling, and on space research—has been so profound and so pervasive as to virtually obscure its humble origins in the quaint, almost amusing, ideas of Wilson concerning hole-electron currents in semiconductors. Yet, it is this theory more than anything else which initiated today's solid-state revolution and which continues to guide electronics scientists in their effort to find even more useful particles and effects within the atomic labyrinths and molecular catacombs of crystalline matter.

By means of such quantum-mechanical "spelunking," in fact, they have now found the following:

Excitons: positively charged holes and negatively charged electrons that travel in pairs and have already spawned a new kind of laser that emits coherent light in a 360° halo instead of a narrow beam. Such lasers may eventually lead to a new type of television display.

Double excitons: combinations of two holes and two electrons that travel in foursomes and may one day be used to smuggle heat, light, and other forms of energy from one point in a material to another without leaving "tracks" in between.

Polarons: free electrons acoustically handcuffed to some of the atoms making up certain crystals. These may make possible a new kind of infrared light detector for use in seeing in the dark.

Phonons: very high-frequency acoustic waves which vibrate constantly along the atomic "jungle gyms" of the solid state. They have already been used to realize superconductive magnets 280,000 times more powerful than the earth's magnetic field and may also be employed eventually in a single chunk of material which will amplify your voice directly when you speak at it.

Plasmons: vibrations that ripple through large clouds or "plasmas" of free holes and electrons in certain crystals. They may soon give birth to a whole new family of components which will operate in very high-frequency microwave and millimeter wave communications systems.

Spin waves: magnetic energy propagated through a crystal by means of atoms whose magnetic poles oscillate in response to certain radio waves, like wheat stalks in a wind. Such waves may eventually be used to amplify radio and radar signals magnetically.

Helicon waves: electromagnetic energy, including light, that travels as slowly as 1 foot per second and moves corkscrew-fashion through ordinarily opaque substances containing solid-state plasmas whose electrons are trapped in a magnetic field. Helicon waves make it possible for microwaves to penetrate metals and, by the same token, may make it possible for them to penetrate the plasma sheath which ordinarily surrounds returning spacecraft and temporarily blacks out their radio communications systems.

These are just some of the quantum chimeras which scientists now have at bay in such unfamiliar solids as gallium arsenide, indium antimonide, cadmium-chromium-selenide, and niobium tin. When captured and tamed, they will undoubtedly give birth to still newer solid-state devices even more sensational, perhaps, than the transistor has turned out to be.

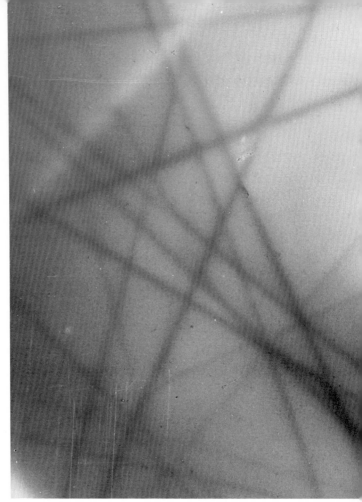

Hallmark of a perfect silicon crystal are these "kikuchi lines" produced by an electron beam which ricocheted from one layer of atoms to another before passing through it.

CHAPTER 3

Mind
over
Matter

In an assault that would gladden the heart of the toughest
battlefield commander, materials scientists are storming across
the atomic frontiers of solid matter in a steadily mounting
campaign to subjugate and exploit the rich electron popula-
tions that inhabit these realms. Committed to this offensive,
in electronics laboratories everywhere, is a host of materials
specialists from chemists and physicists to ceramists, metallurgists, spectroscopists, and crystallographers. Armed with electron microscopes, mass spectrographs, electric furnaces, and an
altogether dazzling array of scientific siege weapons, these men
and women are writing an inspiring saga of dogged research

23

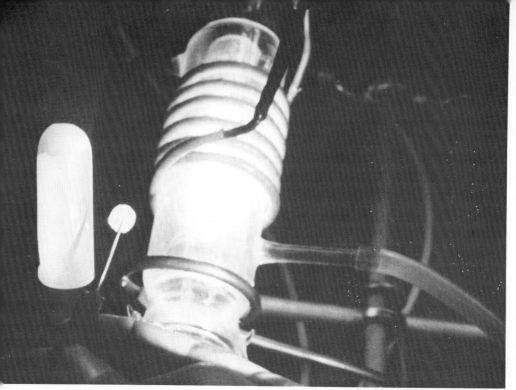

A silicon-on-sapphire wafer containing
several integrated circuits is held in
tweezers beside a freshly grown boule
of sapphire and next to an induction
furnace in which silicon is deposited
on such sapphire wafers.

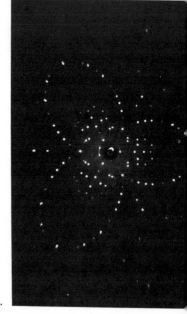

X-ray diffraction of single-
crystal silicon via transmission.

and fundamental discovery that is reshaping the world around us.

With a recent series of lightning incursions into the electron fastnesses of germanium, silicon, and gallium arsenide, for example, scientists have succeeded in bringing electrons locked in the solid state under their dominion sufficiently to produce the transistor and tunnel diode for amplifying radio signals or controlling electron flow in a circuit; the solar cell for converting sunlight to electricity; the thermocouple for transforming heat to significant amounts of electric power; and the injection laser for converting electric current to coherent light.

Before this, materials science in the electronics industry was a sporadic affair which consisted of a few brilliant expeditions into the electronic heartland of matter to discover barium strontium oxides for the production of electrons in vacuum tubes; the ferrites and ferrimagnetic compounds that give computers their memory and electron beams their sense of direction in cathode-ray tubes; and the zinc sulfide–type phosphors that convert the energy of electrons to the images on today's television screens.

The difference between these two sets of exploits—the one occurring within the period 1920 to 1948 and the other within the period 1948 to the present—is a measure, perhaps, of how materials science has broadened in range of interests and grown in sophistication since the birth of the electronics industry a half century ago.

In the early days, electronics scientists and engineers were interested in electrons only after they had been freed from the materials to which they were attached. All they asked of materials science was that it create or uncover substances that, upon the application of heat, would readily spew their electrons into a vacuum, where they could be controlled by electric or magnetic fields.

Later, when the effort to produce television got up steam

in the 1930s, these same engineers requested further that materials be found to convert electron energies to visible light. Materials scientists figured prominently in this search and helped to realize the sulfide and rare earth phosphors that serve the TV industry today.

The achievement of commercial television hinged also on the development of a material which could control the movement of the electron beams that traced pictures on these phosphors by scanning back and forth across them. Here again, materials scientists came to the rescue with a new family of iron oxide compounds called ferrites.

With these and other special materials, the electronics industry was able to produce national telephone networks, radio broadcasting, movie sound systems, the electron microscope, television, microwave radar, and the computer—a rather impressive array of products to derive from a few phosphors and oxides.

By the 1940s, however, electronics customers were demanding more from their equipment than even these materials could provide. What was wanted were radio transmitters and receivers that would operate at extremely high microwave frequencies, computers that would process millions of bits of information per second, and electronic circuitry that was simpler, cheaper, and more reliable.

To meet these new goals, materials researchers at the Bell Telephone Laboratories decided on a novel approach to the most critical function of all electronic circuitry—amplification. Remembering the solid and puzzling galena rectifier used in the early crystal radio sets to detect incoming radio signals, they felt confident that a modern solid-state device could also be developed to amplify such signals. Several years of intensive materials effort followed, culminating in achievement of the germanium point-contact transistor in 1948.

The impact of this development was immediate and far-

Dr. Michael Abrahams is shown
viewing zinc sulfide crystals
through a metallograph and in a
montage which shows at left
what the crystals look like to
him in polarized light.

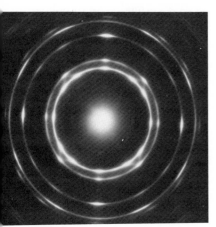

Ring pattern made by electron beam passing through atomic
structure of nickel chromium film one two-millionth of an inch
thick. Bright spots are electron reflections from atomic layers
stacked perfectly atop each other.

reaching. Not only did it give the electronics industry a wholly new breed of circuit component, but it gave materials research within the industry a new set of values and a new sense of purpose. There were many reasons for this.

The transistor represented the first use of a semiconductor to amplify radio waves; it boasted a materials purity down to one foreign atom in every ten million composing it; it was the first application of quantum mechanics to achieve a practical electronic device; it was the first of a new family of components realized solely through materials processing rather than parts fabrication; and it was the first active component to do its work not by releasing electrons to the outside but by controlling them in house, so to speak.

The transistor was only a beginning, however—a first step. Its behavior required a great deal more understanding and elucidation before its performance and reliability could be improved and before still newer devices could be built upon its principles.

At both industrial and university laboratories, interdisciplinary teams of materials scientists were formed to study solids— to elaborate quantum-mechanical theory with regard to them, to develop new means for purifying and synthesizing them, and to map their atomic composition and architecture.

From these concerted investigations, the electronics industry went on to build its first germanium and, later, its first silicon product lines, embracing both transistors and diodes. By 1958, ten years after its announcement, the transistor had fathered a flourishing new semiconductor industry that had attained the $100-million-a-year sales class.

That same year, 1958, saw the next major breakthrough achieved by the new materials science—the tunnel diode developed by Dr. Leo Esaki, then of the Sony Corporation in Japan. Another marvel of processed germanium, this device relied on an obscure outcropping of quantum-mechanical theory called *tunneling*, a term originated by the physicist George Gamow in 1928 to explain how high-speed, negatively charged electrons (beta rays) created in the nuclei of certain atoms, manage to slip unscathed through the screen of intense negative charge which envelops these atoms and which is due to their own orbital electrons.

In the case of Esaki's diode, however, the tunneling involved free electrons slipping through an extremely thin semiconductor junction so dense with negatively charged impurity atoms that electron infiltration through it should have been impossible, according to classical physics. Quantum mechanics said otherwise, and as a matter of fact, tunneling not only occurred in Esaki's diode, but did so at the speed of light, thus promising a new component for electronic circuits that would display switching speeds and electromagnetic sensitivities at least one hundred times greater than transistors.

With this second solid-state development, the pace of materials research quickened considerably. Not only were semiconductors investigated but so were conductors, such as the semimetal bismuth, and insulators, such as barium titanate and calcium tungstate.

On the purification side, new processing techniques, such as *zone refining*, which reduced the impurity levels in certain semiconductor crystals to 1 part in 10 billion, and new structural concepts, such as the *epitaxial layer* and the *planar surface* for improving the electrical performance of transistors and semiconductor diodes, began burrowing their way out of the laboratory and into the production line.

Then, early in 1960, materials scientists working with Dr. Theodore Maiman at the Hughes Research Laboratories in California succeeded in synthesizing a boule of aluminum oxide containing trace amounts of chromium. Later, this artificial ruby gave birth to the first laser, a tiny polished section of the parent crystal that uncorked a tremendous burst of coherent red light when exposed to the brief pulse of a high-intensity xenon flash lamp.

About this time, too, a materials research group under the leadership of Dr. Fred Rosi, of RCA Laboratories, began to canvass the periodic table in search of a practical thermo-electric material for use in the production of electric power directly from heat. Previously most thermoelectric research had been in the area of cooling. Several years before, for instance, Nils Lindenblad, also of RCA, had developed bismuth-telluride alloys to produce thermoelectric cooling on a scale that had made possible the construction of a model room cooled this way. This room was demonstrated to the press in 1956.

Late in 1961, the alternative quest for thermoelectric power also succeeded, and a new germanium-silicon alloy was demon-strated which could take higher temperatures than any thermo-electric substance made or mined. The technology for making these alloys was quickly transferred to the production line and, today, is being used to produce thermocouples which supply electric power from the heat of a nuclear reactor. The first such system was successfully launched into orbit in 1965 as part of the SNAP (Space Nuclear Auxiliary Power) pro-gram being conducted by the National Aeronautics and Space Administration.

At about this same time, another materials research program at RCA, led by Dr. Joseph Hanak, came to fruition with the achievement of a new process for producing niobium-tin films continuously on ribbons of various metals, including stainless steel. The impact of this development has not been fully realized, as yet, but is expected to be prodigious in the field of superconductivity. Such ribbons have since been wound to form several experimental superconductive magnets, one of which is used for nuclear research at Brookhaven National Laboratory on Long Island where it has generated a magnetic

Strain lines swirl around fault in atomic structure of thin germanium crystal shown magnified 320,000 times. Such "dislocations" can help or hinder a material's electronic performance.

field almost 275,000 times stronger than that of the earth. This unit—slightly larger than a football—consumes virtually no power after initial activation by a common storage battery.

In still another area, materials researchers are solving some of the age-old mysteries of solid-state luminescence, photoconductivity, ferrimagnetism, and the conduction of electrons in such fierce-to-make insulators as hafnium and zirconium oxides. To make such exotic materials, scientists often rely on an arc-image furnace, one of the few machines in the world capable of growing them in the single-crystal form required.

To this difficult but challenging worklist must also be added research into photoconductive and photoluminescent materials and studies of one of matter's most bizarre manifestations— hole-electron plasmas in semiconductors.

Fundamentally, then, the electronics revolution of today is a materials revolution blueprinted in quantum mechanics, initiated by the transistor, and led by an enterprising band of materials science adventurers.

Part of the apparatus used by electronics scientists to grow single crystals of various electronically active materials directly from hot gases condensing on a "cold" substrate. Very pure, highly ordered crystals of gallium arsenide and gallium phosphide have been created this way by the process known as vapor phase growth.

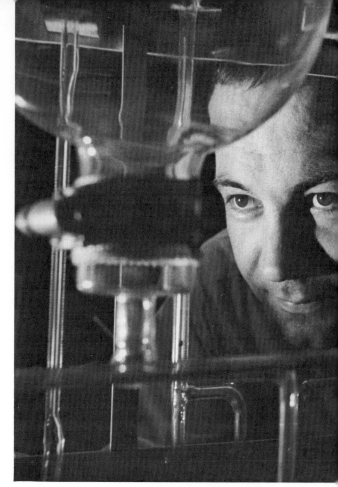

CHAPTER 4

Cultured
Components

Increasing numbers of electronic components are no longer manufactured. They are cultured, instead, like so many electronic pearls in white-hot melts, in nutrient solutions, or in vaporous atmospheres from which they variously coalesce, precipitate, or condense as tiny, gemlike single crystals.

Such are the likes of transistors, for amplifying and switching electric currents in a circuit; semiconductor diodes, for converting alternating to direct current and for producing high-frequency microwaves; and integrated circuits, that perform the functions of whole assemblies of discrete components in fragments of silicon no bigger, sometimes, than the wing of a fly.

Such, too, are solar cells, that convert sunlight directly to electricity to power our nation's space vehicles; masers, for use in amplifying the radio emissions of distant stars and galaxies for study by astronomers; and lasers, for generating intense beams of coherent light, which may one day be used in place of electric currents to carry information in advanced computers and communications systems.

What accounts for this extraordinary metamorphosis in the making of electronic components is the fact that materials scientists have recently learned to re-form many ordinary solids into single crystals whose purity and perfection surpass that of anything produced in nature from snowflake to Hope diamond. When suitably processed, it is these that become the tiny, rugged, low-cost, solid-state devices that have remade the face of the electronics industry since the invention of the transistor twenty-one years ago. The reason they have done so lies, at base, in the nature of the single-crystal state itself.

In essence, single crystals are composed of atoms organized on a large scale in vast three-dimensional mosaics, or "Tinker-Toy" structures, whose architectural order, precision, and symmetry far exceed anything man has yet achieved in cathedral or skyscraper. By contrast, ordinary solids are a hodgepodge of ill-fitting atoms lumped together in jerry-rigged compounds, shot through with fractures, holes, strains, and other architectural anomalies. Indeed, if they were buildings, they would be condemned!

Because of this colossal difference, the same electronic, magnetic, optical, acoustical, and other properties inherent in a polycrystalline solid are invariably more pronounced, more accessible, and far more amenable to control when that solid is recast into single-crystal form.

Another point about single crystals is that they are not built. They are "grown." This occurs in the sense that a stalactite grows from a cave roof, or rock candy grows in a solution

High-energy electron beam slams into a slug of tantalum, heating it to incandescence almost immediately. Beam is produced in a special furnace that can be used to evaporate and deposit in thin-film form almost any material.

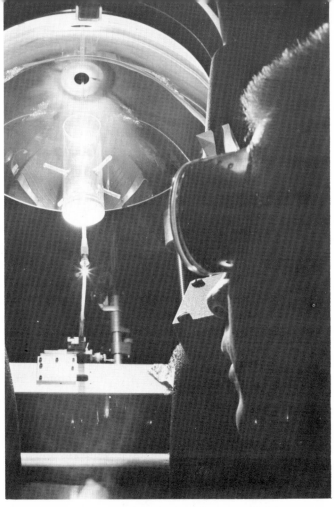

Max Hopkins watches as an arc-image furnace which he built is used to grow a crystal of hafnium oxide in open air. The technique used is an adaptation of Verneuil's famous flame-fusion approach.

of sugar, or frost crystals grow on a windowpane in midwinter. In fact, many of the most valuable constituents of the earth's crust are known to have grown this way over the 4½ billion years since its formation.

Finally, it is of interest too to realize that, with the exception of glasses, most atoms in the gaseous or liquid state prefer to condense into single crystals, upon cooling, because such action represents the line of least resistance for them, in an energy sense. Seen in this light, the growth of single crystals—

whether in the macrocosm of nature or in the microcosm of the laboratory—is a matter of creating the right kind of climate and the proper soil conditions. Mother Nature takes care of the rest.

Within the electronics industry, full appreciation of this fact followed the invention of the transistor and has led since to a novel form of agriculture in which materials scientists and production workers seed, grow, and harvest single crystals of a wide variety of materials which are then cleaned, chemically processed, and packaged for sale in plastic or can, like so many fruits and vegetables.

The Johnny Appleseed of this latter-day agronomy is probably Johann Czochralski, a German physicist, who in 1917 developed a crystal-growing technique that was used eventually to produce the first commercial transistors. Not that efforts to grow crystals had never been made before. Alchemists had succeeded in growing a few during the Middle Ages. Their literature is full of arcane recipes and formulas for making copper sulfate cure-alls and alum astringents in single-crystal form.

Crystal making did not become a serious business until 1902, however, when the French carborundum manufacturer Auguste Verneuil developed his famous *flame-fusion* technique for growing rubies and sapphires of gem quality. What he did was to place a chip of sapphire on a ceramic spit and hold it under an intense flame through which sifted a powder of aluminum oxide (raw sapphire). The powder particles melted instantly in the flame and fell in molten droplets onto the sapphire chip, where they solidified in accordance with the atomic pattern on the surface of the chip. In so doing, they added to the structure of the chip, in the same way that new bricks add to a brick wall. What Verneuil had learned to do was to make the sapphire grow. How this happened could not be explained, however, until 1912 and

Herbert Berman looks through porthole of electron beam
furnace as it evaporates a slug of tantalum.

Edward Miller prepares a high-pressure
autoclave for use in growing single crystals of
gallium phosphide.

the discovery of x-ray diffraction by Max von Laue and others in Germany.

The very short wavelengths and enormous energies of x-rays made it possible for Laue to probe the surface and sub-structure of solid materials for the first time, and to reveal, by x-ray reflections, that single crystals are distinguished by an atomic order and purity undreamed of in the structure of ordinary solids. In fact, he found that single crystals are assembled according to a plan, as though from an architect's blueprint, and that each contains a fundamental unit or cell which is repeated again and again throughout its structure.

Furthermore, he learned that single crystals are built from no more than seven such units, the most common of which is the cube. Although these units frequently consist of atoms of one kind only—carbon, in the case of diamond—he discovered this did not have to be so. The basic unit of table salt crystals, for example, is a cube consisting of sodium and chlorine atoms stationed in alternate corners.

Armed with these insights and inspired by Verneuil's success, Czochralski decided to turn flame fusion on its head by inverting a seed crystal—corresponding to Verneuil's chip—so that it could be lowered to the surface of a hot magma or melt having the same composition, roughly, as the seed itself. He further arranged for the seed to be pulled up very slowly. As anticipated, the melt atoms clung to the seed and added to its structure continuously as it was raised. Thus was born the very powerful crystal-growing technique known as *pulling from the melt*—the technique employed by Drs. John Little and Gordon Teal, then at Bell Laboratories, to grow the single crystals of germanium that gave birth to the manufacture of point-contact transistors in 1949.

In time, however, pulling from the melt turned out to be too arduous and too demanding for use in mass production. Therefore, materials scientists soon resorted to an updated version of still another technique—one originated in 1925 by Dr. Percy Bridgman, a former Harvard professor and recipient of the Nobel Prize. It entailed melting raw materials in an open "boat" which was drawn through a horizontal electric furnace from a hot to a cold region where the melt gradually "froze" into a single crystal. It proved to be simple, effective, and reliable and was eagerly embraced by the fledgling semiconductor industry as the standard method for growing transistor-grade germanium crystals. There were some drawbacks even to this technique, however, the most important being that the crystals it produced still contained too many impurity atoms—one in every ten million to be exact.

At this juncture, William Pfann, of Bell Laboratories, remembered a seemingly minor technique, now called *zone leveling,* which he had stumbled upon as early as 1939 in a search for ways to spread small amounts of the element antimony uniformly through an ingot of lead. It involved melting a narrow zone in the ingot near one end, by placing it at the center of a ring-shaped electric heater, and then slowly drawing the ingot through the heater so that it would melt and jell successively along its entire length. This process had the effect of leveling out the amount of antimony in the bulk of the ingot and, as Pfann now recalled, even tended to sweep it out altogether, since antimony has a lower freezing point than lead and wanted to remain in solution even while the lead was solidifying.

A reappraisal of this earlier technique now led Pfann to conclude that, with suitable modification, it might be used not only to level out impurities in a crystal, but actually to remove them. This would be accomplished, he reasoned, if several melted zones were passed through the crystal in succession. On first try, he succeeded beyond his wildest dreams. The passage of several zones through the germanium crystals he was growing refined them to a level of one impurity atom

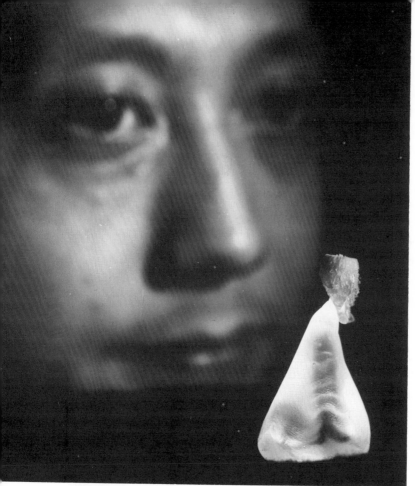

Looking like one of the three wise men in the Christmas story, this single crystal of spinel was grown from a powder cone (top) by means of the flame-fusion, or Verneuil process. Thin slices cut from it are being investigated for use as insulating substrates for integrated circuits.

Flux growth—precipitating crystallites of one material from a molten bath of another—is accomplished in this intensely hot electric furnace. Rare-earth-containing phosphors for use in the screens of color TV sets are grown this way.

in every ten billion, yielding crystals a thousand times purer than the one used to make the first transistor! In addition to this immediate benefit, the technique—instantly dubbed *zone refining* to distinguish it from *zone leveling*—provided Dr. William Shockley, a coworker of Pfann's, with a material pure enough to make possible a basic change in the structure of the transistor itself, from the original point-contact to the far more subtle junction type that is standard today.

Although zone refining removed impurities as a limiting factor in the performance of transistors, it did not remove the problem of crystalline imperfections. In crystals generally, these included such *bêtes-noires* as vacancies (missing atoms), interstitial defects (atoms out of position), and dislocations (whole layers of atoms that suddenly terminate halfway through a crystal, instead of continuing to the other side). In transistor crystals, specifically, it was dislocations that gave the greatest trouble by snagging and diverting substantial fractions of the electrons that flowed through them when in operation.

In 1954, Dr. Fred Rosi, currently in charge of RCA Laboratories' materials and devices research programs, proposed and then proved that such defects could be greatly reduced, if not eliminated, by making certain that the growing crystal was kept continuously flat on the end where it touched the hot melt. Simple as this requirement seems, its discovery was a major step forward and did for dislocations what zone refining had done for impurities. In fact, when the two techniques were subsequently combined in the growth of germanium crystals, the resulting transistors easily outperformed the best electron tubes then available.

Germanium was not the only semiconducting material being grown and processed into transistors at this time. A strong effort was also being made in behalf of silicon. A major stumbling block here, though, was that molten silicon, at

2600°F, behaves like an acid. It attacks and erodes almost any container it touches and reacts with almost any atmosphere containing oxygen.

Many ingenious measures were evolved to circumvent these difficulties—high-temperature graphite pots were developed to contain the melt; silicon crystals were grown, via the Czochralski rather than the Bridgman technique, to reduce chemical interaction with the sides of the pot; growth was accomplished in a closed argon or other inert environment—but all fell short. Then, in 1953, at the Fort Monmouth Research Laboratories of the U.S. Army Signal Corps, Paul Keck and Marcel Golay collaborated in the development of a method they dubbed the *floating zone* technique. It proved to be the long-sought breakthrough needed for growing single-crystal silicon of the highest purity.

The technique entailed use of a stick compacted out of raw silicon powders and clamped upright in an electric furnace. The stick was first converted to a single crystal by passing a molten zone up through it from bottom to top. (The zone did not collapse and leak down the sides of the stick, as might have been expected, because its surface tension was too great.) Then it was zone-refined. The result was a long single crystal of surpassing structural perfection and chemical purity. It is this technique, coupled with such intrinsic features as high-temperature performance and an ability to be insulated by means of its own surface oxides (an important consideration for integrated circuits), that has conspired to make silicon the dominant material in semiconductor devices today.

Based upon the materials knowledge and materials control achieved through this and other work over the past century, the electronics industry is now engaged in a vast effort to reconstitute as many materials as possible in single-crystal form in a quest for newer and still more versatile components. This effort is being prosecuted not only in the elemental solids but in the endless variety of compounds and alloys into which these can be combined as well.

More produce than product, transistors and their single-crystal progeny are today transforming the electronic components industry from a manufacturing to an agricultural activity whose bumper yields are feeding a growing population of new and revolutionary consumer, industrial, and military equipment.

Robert Gange points to the solder pads on an experimental superconductive memory plane which can store 16,384 bits of computer data.

CHAPTER 5

Electronic
Films

Though they are not produced in wide-screen CinemaScope, have never won an Oscar, and cannot be viewed on "Saturday Night at the Movies," electronic films are already smash hits in many important sectors of modern electronics technology. Increasingly, they are being "booked" into television equipment, computer logic and memory circuits, two-way communications systems, missile and spacecraft controls, and of course, pocket radios. In fact, if present trends continue, they may yet make the electronics industry the new "film capital" of the world.

As distinguished from photographic film, electronic films

45

are delicate tattoos of electronically active material condensed, for the most part, from hot vapors onto cold, hard insulating surfaces such as glass. Depending on the materials used and the manner in which they are laid down, such films—many of them ten times thinner than the shimmering coat of an ordinary soap bubble—may act singly or in combination as whole electronic circuits or simply as components thereof, from transistors and diodes to resistors, capacitors, and interconnection paths.

At electronics laboratories around the world, these films have been under investigation for many years and are presently being explored in programs that may eventually lead to a TV camera only half an inch square; a hand-held, battery-operated computer; an exotic form of computer memory that would use the phenomenon of superconductivity to store a quarter million bits of information on a glass slide half a foot square; a new type of video tape which can store pictures optically for later readout by an electron beam; and a revolutionary kind of integrated circuitry for application across the board, in all forms of electronic equipment.

Interest in electronic films arose in the early 1920s following the landmark investigations of Irving Langmuir and Kenneth Kingdon into the nature and dynamics of atomic monolayers—thin layers of various materials one atom thick. The development about the same time of x-ray diffraction and similar investigative techniques led other researchers to extend these studies to include thin metal and metal oxide films that evinced valuable optical and electronic properties.

Electronics scientists were particularly intrigued because of the problems they were experiencing in improving the operation of electron tube cathodes—the tiny metal founts out of which pour the electron beams used to amplify radio waves. They had already found, as early as 1905, that metal cathodes worked much better and produced far more electrons if they were painted with a film of barium strontium oxide. Just how the oxide helped, however, was a puzzle which, it was hoped, the new findings concerning thin films might explain.

Thin-film research began in earnest thereafter, both here and in Europe. One of its early dividends was the thoriated tungsten cathode—a tungsten filament whose surface is impregnated with the element thorium. Capable of withstanding very high temperatures while putting out torrents of electrons, this cathode is still one of the best available for fashioning the powerful signals that make worldwide radio communications possible.

Far more spectacular in its way, however, was the development, during this same period, of the photocathode—a thin film which would release electrons when bombarded with light. This achievement was the first truly dramatic application of thin-film technology to electronics, for it became the heart of the television camera tube as well as of other conversion and imaging tubes, such as the photomultiplier, and ultraviolet and infrared detectors.

Such films, many of them the creations of Dr. Alfred Sommer, of RCA, are exotic mixtures of metals and oxides (such as potassium-cesium-antimony) evaporated onto glass windows, under high vacuum, in diaphanous layers from 200 to 800 angstroms thick. (If dollar bills were 1 angstrom thick, a million could be stacked in the same space taken up by a single conventional bill!)

When light from a scene to be televised strikes this film on the inside surface of a TV camera tube, electrons, in numbers directly proportional to the intensity of the light, spring inward toward a glass target on which they collect in a pattern that is the electrical equivalent of the visible scene. An electron beam on the other side of the target then scans the pattern and is reflected by it to a greater or lesser extent depending on the strength of the charge at any one point in the pattern. Thus, the electron beam, as reflected from the pattern, becomes a pulsating current that varies in intensity, as did the light which struck the photocathode originally. This current is then amplified, sent to a TV transmitter for conversion to a microwave signal, and broadcast.

At about this time also, still another material—silver-oxide—cesium—was perfected. It used a like principle to detect infrared radiation and became the basis for the sniperscope and snooperscope, used by American soldiers during World War II to spot enemy infiltrators in the dark.

While research on thin films continued to be done through the 1940s, it was temporarily eclipsed by development of the transistor in 1948. Physicists, chemists, and metallurgists focused instead on studies of the bulk properties of semiconductive materials such as germanium and silicon.

For a time, transistors, semiconductor diodes, and other solid-state components born of this effort seemed to sweep all else before them. In small-signal applications, such as hearing aids and pocket radios, and in high-speed switching applications, such as computers, these devices seemed to have all the advantages and none of the disadvantages of electron tubes. They were small, they operated at room temperature and they were highly reliable, and potentially very inexpensive to manufacture. This was in the early 1950s. By the late 1950s, however, as such devices attempted to compete with tubes in high-frequency applications, as they sought to attain really high-speed switching, as they ran up against industrial and military circuits which employed high voltages and operated in punishing environments, their inherent electrical limitations and their sensitivity to surface deterioration began to become manifest.

At this juncture, two major developments of a pseudo-thin-film nature were reported by Bell Telephone Laboratories. The first was a technique for insulating the active areas of silicon devices by growing a silicon oxide film over them. This led

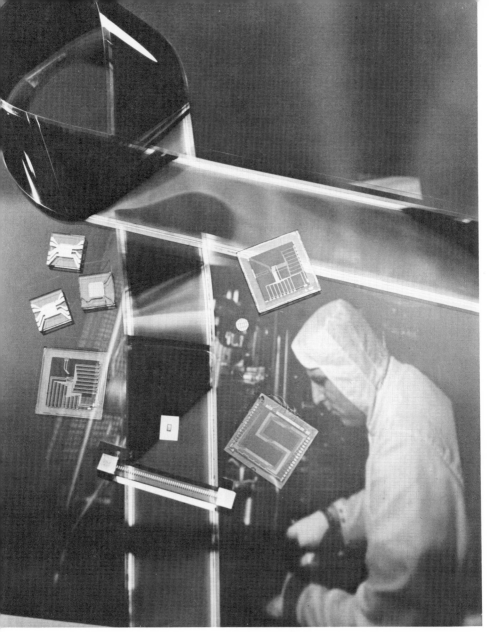

Thin-film transistor components, silicon-on-sapphire circuits, superconductive memory planes, and a unique dielectric tape for use in a special space camera are examples of thin-film technology here displayed on a background that includes a technician preparing a vacuum-deposition furnace for use.

eventually to the famous *planar* process, whereby such films are used like masking tape—both to define and to isolate the areas in the 25-cent-piece-sized silicon wafers in which today's transistors are fabricated. These insulating layers are now grown on virtually all silicon devices as a matter of course and are usually no more than 5,000 angstroms thick—the wavelength of green light. They sharply reduce the problem of surface contamination in transistors.

The second development, announced in 1960, was *epitaxy* —the growth on these same wafers of single-crystal skins which are exactly like the wafers structurally but which differ significantly in their electrical properties.

Taken together, these two techniques not only overcame the limitations impeding further advances in semiconductor technology at the time, but equally important, they set the stage for the evolution of integrated circuitry. Today, integrated circuits are built into silicon wafers by chemically etching holes in the planar oxide down to the epitaxial layer. Chemical impurities are then driven into this layer to form the devices. After that, the holes are resealed by growing more oxide over them or by evaporating metal contacts into them. Metal pathways interconnecting these contacts, plus such passive components as resistors and capacitors, are then evaporated down on the oxide, where needed to complete the circuits.

Thus, by 1960, transistors and complete integrated circuits were and still are being made in layers of single-crystal, epitaxial silicon coated with silicon oxide. Such layers, incidentally, are only 10,000 to 20,000 angstroms thick—thinner than frost on a windowpane.

Thin as these layers are, however, they are not considered to be thin films, in the usual sense, because they are inextricably anchored to a supporting silicon base that is many thousandths of an inch thick and that is cheek-by-jowl a part of them. So

Dr. Charles Mueller holds a tiny square of silicon-on-sapphire material which incorporates four integrated circuits which are the equivalent of the transistor circuit shown behind it.

Dr. Kari Karstadt holds up two quartz crystals on which elements have been deposited that could one day lead to a sonic-film memory—a memory for computers which magnetically stores information that can be retrieved by launching a sonic pulse down the crystals.

Dr. Paul Weimer displays three glass slides holding the thin-film equivalent of the vacuum tube vidicon in his left hand. In the background is a thin-film transistor circuit magnified on the screen of a Nikon comparator.

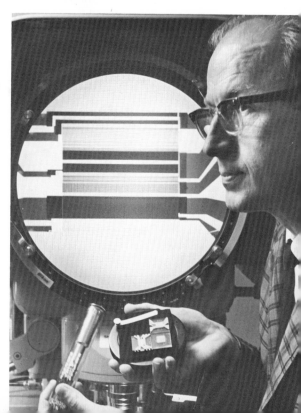

much so, in fact, that this base produces a parasitic electrical effect—a kind of electromagnetic drag—that inhibits the operation of the devices as a whole and degrades their performance.

It was the quest for a way to obviate this parasitic effect, as well as to give new dimension to the concept of integrated circuitry, that led Dr. Paul Weimer, of RCA Laboratories, to a line of research that, in 1961, produced the first thin-film transistor (TFT)—a new type of transistor consisting of layers of polycrystalline cadmium sulfide, silicon oxide, and gold evaporated on a glass slide in a sandwich 2,000 to 10,000 angstroms thick.

Although it is not yet so fast nor so reliable as its planar, epitaxial, single-crystal silicon cousin, the TFT has many advantages in its own right and is currently being tested, together with other thin-film components, in compact experimental arrays which may one day lead to a flat TV camera "eye" only ½ inch square and a hand-held digital computer capable of operating from a flashlight battery.

Taking a different approach to the parasitic problem, stemming from the supporting silicon wafer of conventional integrated circuits, scientists at Autonetics, a division of North American Rockwell, in California, and at RCA, began wondering, about 1963, if they could not separate the planar and epitaxial layers from their supporting silicon by growing them on a single-crystal insulating material so close to silicon in structure that the layers would not know the difference. The insulating material chosen was sapphire (aluminum oxide). Although not perfect, the match between the silicon layers and the sapphire proved to be so good it was immediately possible to grow some types of diodes and transistors this way and to show that they did not suffer any parasitic limitations.

So promising is this new silicon-on-sapphire technology, in fact, that scientists hope to use it to achieve transistors and integrated circuits capable of handling radio frequencies up to a billion cycles per second for application in new forms of radar that scan the sky electronically and in new "scratch-pad" computer memories that can retrieve a bit of information in the time it takes a light beam to travel 10 feet.

Not to be outdone by researchers foraging in the virgin territory of thin-film semiconductor physics, other scientists and engineers recently have been equally enterprising in their application of thin-film technology. For example, computer memories are being developed which use the interaction of sound waves and electrical pulses to change the magnetic character of tiny areas in a thin permalloy film into either of two possible states. These states correspond to the 1 and 0 of binary code—the language of computers. Which of the two states these permalloy areas are forced to take can be sensed later by the mere expedient of sending a sonic pulse through the film to read them. Such memories may some day store 100,000 bits of information on a glass slide only 10 inches long and 1 inch wide.

Also under development by industrial scientists and engineers is a superconductive memory that is a sandwich of tin, lead, and silicon oxide films that store computer 1s and 0s in the form of electrical currents that can persist forever, so long as the memory is kept in liquid helium at a temperature only a few degrees above absolute zero. Such a memory, in final form, will consist of a flat glass plate on which the thin-film sandwich is deposited. It is estimated that one such "plane" should be capable of storing 250,000 bits of information in an area only 5 inches on a side and only 50,000 angstroms, or two ten-thousandths of an inch thick.

An equally novel thin-film structure presently under development is a dielectric tape for use in a special camera that could take closeup pictures of planets and relay them back to earth electronically at five times the speed possible with present space cameras. It consists of thin films of copper-gold, a photoconductive material, and a polystyrene coating, all laid down on a plastic ribbon.

When light falls on it, an electric charge pattern, varying in strength in proportion to the intensity variations in the light itself, builds up on the polystyrene. When an electron beam scans across this charge pattern, it causes tiny electric currents to flow through the tape in direct proportion to the voltage variations in the charge pattern. These, in turn, produce a TV signal. In effect, this novel device is like a standard vidicon TV camera, but it has several superior features, including the ability to store an image until it is wanted.

"Electronics all in rime," one wit has called this remarkable technology for building electronic devices in films whose thickness is measured in wavelengths of light. Whether, in fact, all types of electronic components can or will be produced this way eventually is problematical. One thing is certain, however. There is a new generation of "film stars" coming along in the electronics field that has never heard of Hollywood.

Atomic structure at the surface of a tungsten hemisphere of approximately 700-angstrom radius, as seen by the field ion microscope developed by Dr. Erwin Müller at Pennsylvania State University. Magnification is 2,300,000×.

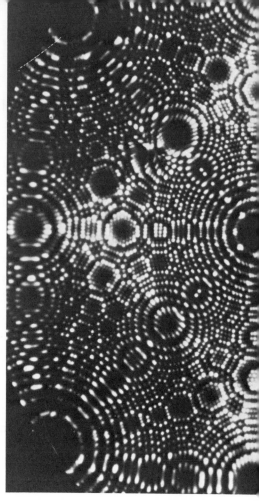

CHAPTER 6

The
Superficial
Electron

Beauty is only skin deep, they say. And so, it turns out, is most of electronics.

Electron tubes, transistors, waveguides for carrying microwave signals, office copying machines, scanning electron microscopes, TV cameras and receivers—all depend, at bottom, on the behavior of electrons at, near, or on a solid surface, or on a frontier (interface) where two surfaces or states of matter merge.

As if to underscore this fact, electronics scientists and researchers, in recent years, have been investigating several new species of surface phenomena such as surface superconduc-

57

tivity, surface sound waves, surface light emission, and the remarkable electronic properties of such atomic structures as surface states and interface states.

From these studies, eventually, may come electron tubes that operate "cold" like transistors; tiny microwave circuits that process radar and TV signals by first converting them to high-frequency sound waves; materials that are superconductive at room temperature (lose all resistance to the flow of electric current) and may make possible a kind of cable that will carry electric power over long distances without loss; and integrated circuits whose functional complexity per unit of area may one day rival that of the human brain.

Already, in fact, such studies have produced a new form of transistor, the Insulated Gate Field-Effect Transistor (IGFET) that is the solid-state counterpart of an electron tube; a new photomultiplier, or light detector, that can sense light that is too weak or flashes too briefly to be seen by the human eye and that could revolutionize studies in the nuclear, biological, and astronomical sciences; a novel type of electron tube that

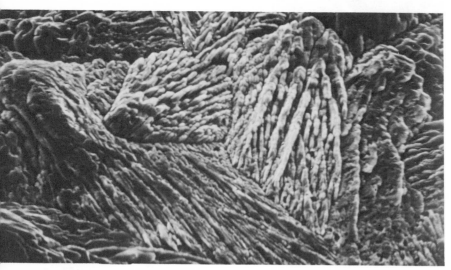

Pressed zinc oxide. Magnification is
540×.

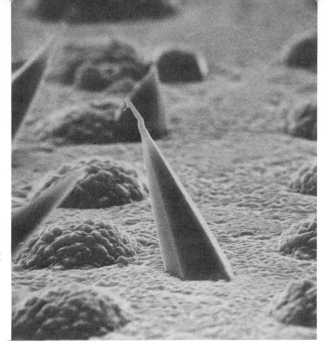

Germanium, single-crystal whiskers growing out of a germanium substrate. Magnification is 1,000×.

can store TV pictures for hours, even with the power off, and could form the basis for a new type of computer memory, or long-term display device; and the most compact general-purpose computer yet attempted.

The superficial nature of useful electronic phenomena was first revealed in 1729, in London, when Stephen Grey conducted an ingenious experiment whereby he showed that two oak blocks of identical size, one solid and one hollow, would store the same amount of static electricity and no more. Obviously, he reasoned, the interior of the solid block played no part in the storage, or it would have held more.

Another indication was seen in 1777 by Georg Lichtenberg, in Germany, when he accidentally discovered that dust collected in beautiful sunburst patterns on the surface of resin cakes which had been subjected to strong electrical discharges. Out of such an apparently trivial observation, incidentally, have now come the electrostatic dust precipitator and the multi-million-dollar electrostatic copying industry!

Once again, in 1836, the importance of surfaces was confirmed by the epic studies of Jöns Jacob Berzelius, in Sweden.

He found that many chemical reactions take place only in the presence of a material that acts as a matchmaker. It promotes the reaction, but does not participate in it. He called the phenomenon *catalysis,* and pointed out that, often, only the surface of the catalyst is involved in producing the reaction.

It is just such surface catalysis that is exploited in the "cracking towers" of the petrochemical industry to extract gasoline, kerosene, ammonia, and nitrates for explosives and fertilizers from crude oil. Berzelius could not know it, at the time, but catalysis has turned out to be an electronic phenomenon as, indeed, is all chemistry.

Surfaces next figured prominently in the thinking of Lord Rayleigh, the British pioneer in acoustical theory. In a major work, published in 1877, he postulated, among other things, the existence of sound waves that travel only on the surfaces of materials. These are now called *Rayleigh waves,* in his honor, and may be compared to the waves that travel on the surface of the ocean in contradistinction to those that travel through its bulk. Both are essentially acoustic—they represent the successive displacement and recoil of atoms or molecules in an elastic medium—but become differentiated due to the fact that the medium changes spectacularly from a three-dimensional form, in the bulk, to a two-dimensional form at the surface.

Such sound waves can have very high frequencies—frequencies comparable to those of microwaves in the electromagnetic spectrum—though they propagate 100,000 times more slowly than the latter. It has also been learned, since interest in Rayleigh waves was revived about 1966, that they can be generated, guided, amplified, and otherwise processed on the surfaces of various materials in the manner of microwaves. As a result, several electronics laboratories are attempting to develop a new breed of integrated circuitry that will convert microwaves to their Rayleigh-wave equivalents for subsequent

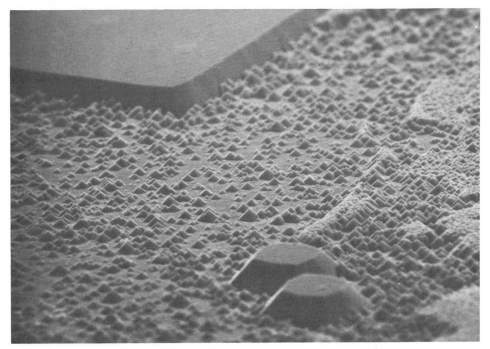

Silicon "mesas" grown on a sapphire substrate. Magnification is 350×.

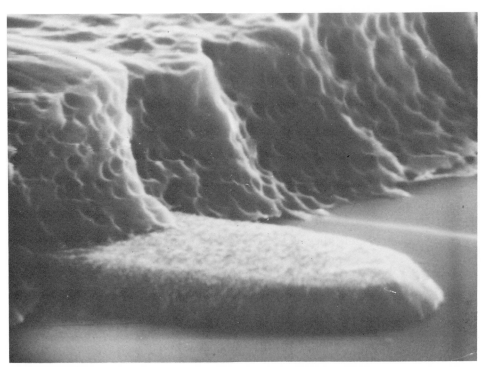

Portion of a silicon epitaxial transistor showing an area 3 to 4 microns deep. The frothy wall is an aluminum contact etched to reveal an epitaxial silicon emitter on a silicon oxide substrate. Magnification is 7,650×.

manipulation in communications, radar, and other high-frequency equipment. When realized, such circuits are expected to be more rugged, more reliable, and more compact than anything yet achieved in the microwave field.

The exact nature and structure of solid surfaces, especially those of metals, became a matter of obsessive interest following the discoveries of Thomas Edison, Heinrich Hertz, Louis Austin, and Hermann Starke at the turn of the century.

In the course of efforts to build an electric light bulb in 1883, Edison discovered that an electric current will flow between two unconnected wires in a vacuum, providing they are linked to an outside electrical source that causes one of them to get hot. The phenomenon was called the Edison effect, for a time, but is now referred to as *thermionic emission*.

In 1887, Hertz added to the confusion by discovering that certain metal surfaces give off weak electric currents when irradiated with selected frequencies of light. The effect is called *photoemission*.

Finally, in 1902—four years after the epochal discovery of the electron by Joseph Thomson, in England—Austin and Starke, in Germany, discovered the phenomenon of *secondary emission:* high-energy electrons, bombarding the surfaces of certain metals, cause them to eject more electrons than they absorb.

Electrical engineers rushed to exploit these strange and marvelous phenomena and, in the course of the next forty years, succeeded in using them to produce the vacuum-tube triode and radio, the image orthicon and television, and the photomultiplier and the scanning electron microscope. Even before they did so, however, theoretical physicists the world over fell to grappling with the basic question of why some surfaces emit electrons, while others do not.

In this connection, Owen Richardson, in 1903, observed that the mathematical formula used to describe the emission of electrons from the surface of a material had a certain constant associated with it. After considerable rumination, he concluded this constant must represent the amount of energy required by free electrons at the surface of a material to work their way off into space or into another material. Appropriately, he called this escape energy the *work function* and noted that it would be different for different materials.

Soon after, it was determined by others that man-made compounds of high and low work-function materials often had lower work functions than their separate constituents. In fact, it was the synthesis of such new compounds that led Dr. Alfred Sommer, of RCA, to develop the world's most efficient photoemitters, starting in the late 1930s; and Drs. Ralph Simon and Brown Williams, more recently, to develop the world's most efficient secondary emitter.

Still, work function was a descriptive term, not an explanation. What gave rise to it? The question could not be answered until something more definitive could be learned about the topography—the atomic landscape, if you will—of solid surfaces.

The first significant step in that direction was made in 1927 when Clinton Davisson and Lester Germer, at Bell Telephone Laboratories, performed their historic study of single-crystal nickel. They directed a beam of low-energy electrons against the crystal, whereupon the beam was diffracted by the atoms there onto photographic film. The fact that it was diffracted (behaved like a light beam), instead of scattered, proved that electrons have the properties both of particles and of waves, and this was surprising enough. Almost as surprising, however, was the further observation that the diffraction patterns registered on the film from deep within the crystal were strikingly different from those produced by the crystal surface. Obviously, there was a profound structural difference between the two.

Though oblivious to this work at the time, Igor Tamm, in

The groove of a phonograph record showing modulation along the edges. Magnification is 228×.

Russia, was also curious about the structure of single-crystal surfaces and, in 1932, he applied the new mathematics of quantum mechanics to the problem. He quickly concluded, as a result, that the electrical properties of crystalline surfaces must also be quite different from those of their interiors, largely due to something he called *surface states*—tiny architectural aberrations that develop as the surface is formed.

From these and other studies over the next several decades has come the following understanding of those differences. It appears that the electrical forces, or *bonds,* that hold crystal atoms together are perfectly balanced in the crystal interior, but are unbalanced at its surface. This is so because the surface atoms, having no atoms above them, are left with "dangling" electrons that can only be neutralized by capturing vagrant charges in the surrounding environment or by rearranging themselves in a cooperative effort to reduce their exposed charges to a minimum. In doing so, however, the surface atoms are forced to break the electrical and architectural symmetry established by the interior atoms with the result that they produce surface states—sites to which free electrons or other charged particles are attracted, and by which they are trapped. It has even been determined that there are two types of surface states—called "slow" or "fast" depending on how long they can keep a charge trapped.

An intriguing theory, to be sure. But it failed to win much acceptance until 1947, when John Bardeen at Bell Telephone Laboratories proposed that, in the case where a metal point is put in contact with a semiconductor surface such as that of silicon, surface states on the silicon should produce a charged layer (now called a *space charge region*) just below the surface that will rectify (convert) alternating to direct current.

Such an effect had been known to exist since the early 1920s when it was used in the form of a metal point, or "cat's whisker," in contact with a semiconductive galena crystal, to make the crystal radio set possible. The effect was thought to

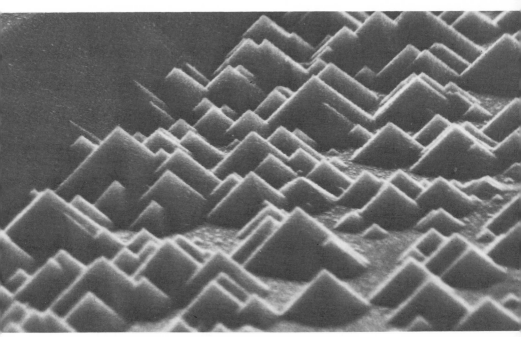

Silicon layer deposited on a sapphire substrate. Tiny "pyramids" are outcroppings of silicon. Magnification is 2,000×.

stem, however, from the fact that the metal point and the crystal had different work functions. The metal point was believed to act like a sponge and to sop up free electrons from the semiconductor the moment the two were put in contact. This had the further effect of creating a positively charged region in the semiconductor just below the contact. Finally, it was assumed that the higher work function of the metal point prevented the return of the electrons kidnapped from the crystal even when a small negative voltage was applied to the metal. When the point was part of an ac circuit and went negative, therefore, nothing happened. When it went positive, on the other hand, free electrons from deeper regions of the crystal now rushed up into it. Such a rectifying contact was dubbed a *Schottky barrier* in tribute to Walter Schottky, in Germany, one of the first to describe it.

Not so, said Bardeen. This was not the way it happened, and to prove it, he joined with a coworker, Walter Brattain; together they set about making and analyzing point contacts on semiconductor surfaces. In one such experiment, they used two point contacts on the top surface of a germanium crystal and a conventional contact on the bottom surface. The result was the point-contact transistor—the first transistor ever built.

That same year, 1948, in the course of trying to build a better transistor, William Shockley and Gerald Pearson, also of Bell Laboratories, decided to see if they could control the flow of electrons through a semiconductor crystal indirectly. They chose a silicon crystal and planned to control electric current moving through it, not by raising and lowering the number of free electrons directly with metal contacts, but, from outside, by applying an alternating electric field whose changing values, positive to negative, would determine how many electrons got through at any given moment in the manner of a faucet or valve.

The experiment failed. Only 10 percent of the current

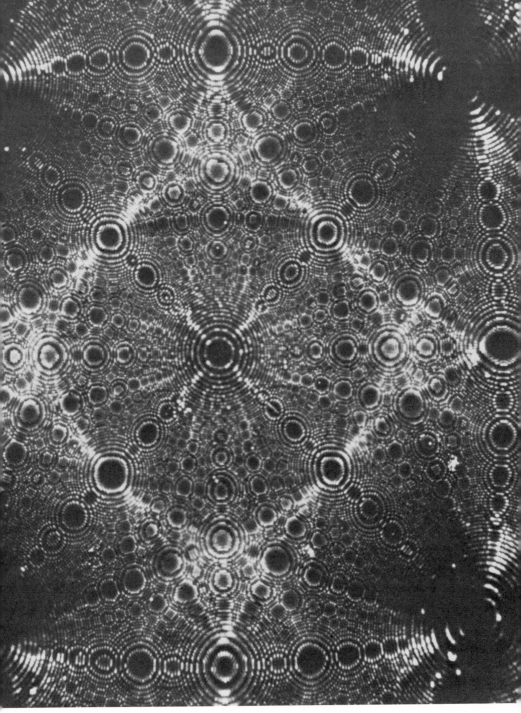

Atomic structure at the surface of a platinum-crystal hemisphere of approximately 1,500-angstrom radius. FIM micrograph.

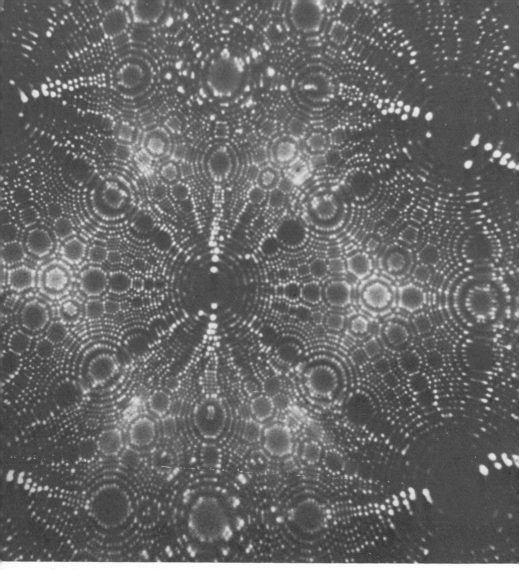

Atomic structure at the surface of an iridium-crystal
hemisphere. FIM micrograph.

moving through the crystal could be controlled this way. The
reason? Electrons in the first onrush of current were captured
by surface states, as Bardeen had anticipated, and thereafter,
they acted to block further penetration of the silicon surface
by the outside electric field. The reality of surface states had
at last been demonstrated.

The failure of this field-effect experiment convinced Shockley that a better transistor would not be built until it could be made completely independent of its surfaces. Finally, in 1949, he succeeded in doing just that by developing the *junction transistor,* a device whose active regions lie well below their crystalline surface. It has since superseded the point-contact type completely.

There the matter rested until 1959, ten years later, when Martin Atalla, at Bell, discovered that the surface states on silicon could be greatly reduced, if not eliminated, by roasting the silicon in an oxygen environment and causing a thin layer of silicon oxide to form on its surface. The effect of the oxygen was to neutralize most of the dangling electron bonds of the silicon surface atoms which gave rise to the surface states. In addition, of those states left, the slow ones tended to retreat to the top of the oxide, while the fast ones remained, in reduced number, at the interface between the oxide and silicon.

Could an electric field be applied through that oxide to control an electric current moving in the space charge region just below the silicon surface? Steven Hofstein and Frederick Heiman, two youthful members of the research staff at RCA Laboratories, were convinced it could. They set out at once to prove it and, in 1963, reported development of what was to become the first practical insulated gate field-effect transistor. It consisted of two metal contacts on the silicon and one on the oxide and showed that the original idea of Shockley and Pearson had been right after all. Insulated gate field-effect transistors are now competing strongly with their junction counterparts in everything from integrated circuits and computer memories to radios, phonographs, and TV sets. They may yet supplant them, in fact.

For the present, at least, it is from the shallows, not the depths, of the solid state that electronics scientists are hauling their richest device catches and newest phenomenological finds.

Dr. Maurice Coutts watches intently as the beam of an electron microscope scans a sample of material under investigation.

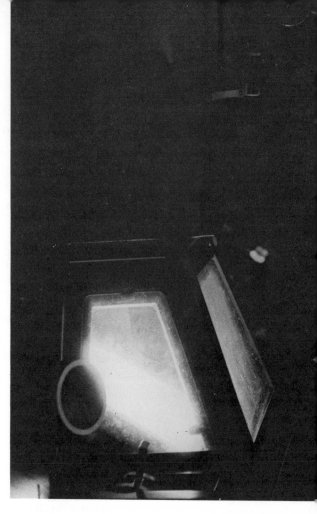

CHAPTER 7

Machines
of Science

As practiced today, electronics science is the meteorology of matter. Air currents, inversion layers, electric storms, tornadoes, thunder, heat, humidity, drought, smog—all have their counterparts in the various atomic atmospheres we call substances. In fact the 104 natural and man-made elements which scientists have now identified and stuffed into the pigeonholes of the periodic table are really nothing more than dense cloud formations of atoms. They grow, thin, condense, and evaporate in response to the ebb and flow of lambent energy in the same way that cumulus, cirrus, and other natural cloud formations materialize and dissipate in the sky.

It is for this reason that matter, especially solid matter, has always been so difficult to explore. Materials scientists—like meteorologists—have had to be content with observations and remote measurements from the ground, so to speak. In the first 7,000 years of recorded history, the best this had allowed men to do was to saw wood, chip stone, bake clay, fuse glass, and smelt iron. Not until the last century did anyone suspect the electronic nature of matter, and not until this century has anyone been able to do anything about it.

How man has since capitalized on that monumental perception to create machines that do everything, from brushing his teeth to lobbing him into outer space, is already well celebrated. Less recognized, perhaps, is how it has led to the creation of strange and formidable machines that may yet carry man to a complete understanding of matter in all its forms.

Although they are legion in number and groan under such fearsome titles as electron microscope, Van de Graaff accelerator, x-ray diffractometer, emission spectrograph, they are a tame bestiary of high-voltage, high-vacuum, high-priced monsters, whose care and feeding constitute a good part of what goes on in a modern research laboratory. Also they are neither so frightening nor so enigmatic as their names might suggest.

For the most part, there are four species of such laboratory leviathans, classed according to whether they produce electron beams, photon (light) beams, ion beams, or neutron beams. An exception is the computer.

The purpose of those that "finger" matter with high-speed beams of electrons is to study the physical structure—the architecture—of solids. Thus, the electron microscope produces a beam of 100,000-volt electrons that are focused by magnetic "lenses" into an electronic needle which probes, in vacuum, the surface and atomic underpinnings of various materials. This beam can reveal details down to two atomic spacings, in some cases, and can magnify a specimen up to 250,000 times.

When such a beam passes through a material, it is captured on photographic film where a picture of what it has "seen" is instantly fixed for study. By this means, scientists are able to examine the size, shape, and distribution of particles in the sample, to elucidate its surface structure, and to detect hidden flaws.

A variation on the electron microscope is the *electron beam scanner*, whose focus is deliberately kept to about 2,000 atomic diameters—about one one-hundredth the width of a human hair. In one version of this machine, the beam penetrates its target to a depth of about half a thousandth of an inch, whereupon it is absorbed. Electrons in the target material itself, however, disturbed by the passage of the beam, rebound from the sample and are detected by a scintillation counter (a crystal that emits tiny flashes of light wherever electrons strike

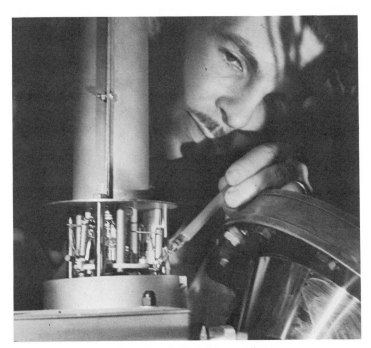

J. Roger Woolsten seems enmeshed in the innards of a mass spectrograph which is used to determine impurity levels down to one part in a billion.

it). The face of the counter, in turn, is watched by a photomultiplier, which converts the flashes to a continuous electric current that varies as a function of their brightness. This current is then fed to a TV kinescope on which an actual picture of the sample subsurface is made to appear. Since the active parts of most transistors and integrated circuits go no deeper than half a thousandth of an inch, the electron beam scanner makes it possible to study their structural features in all three dimensions.

The *Van de Graaff accelerator,* on the other hand, develops a 1-million-volt beam of electrons so powerful that, when it bursts into a material, structural damage results. Such a device is currently teaching scientists how electrons in the Van Allen belts, girding the earth, slowly rob solar cells of their ability to generate electric power for space satellites.

Equally intriguing in the category of electron beam machines is the *electron beam furnace.* Built like a diving helmet with one huge, cyclopean eye that stares out from the top of two spindly legs, this brachycephalic basilisk wears in its headdress an electron gun that plunges down into a cavity behind its eyelike faceplate. When a vacuum pump exhausts this cavity of air, the electron gun erupts with a steady beam of 30,000-volt electrons so intense it will vaporize any known material in seconds.

What is novel about this furnace is that it delivers heat only at the focal point of its electron beam. For this reason, it can be used to create new compounds and new alloys by vaporizing high-temperature materials and allowing them to condense jointly on a cool surface somewhere else in the furnace. Rhenium-tantalum alloys and malleable sheets of molybdenum have been produced this way for the first time.

In the class of scientific machines that do their work with beams of photons—light, x-rays, gamma rays—the *metallograph* deserves mention. It is the last word in classical microscopy, having an ability, in white light, to magnify a specimen up to 1,600 times for direct viewing by the naked eye. For photographic film, it can nearly double this magnification to 3,000 times. It is still the best instrument for direct optical study of the surface structure of materials.

The workhorse of this genre of machines, however, is the *x-ray diffractometer.* Soft x-rays (unlike the hard ones used in medicine and industry) are generated in a cylindrical housing at the hub of a circular platform and released through four portholes to fall on targets set at various angles and distances in front of them. Depending on their strength, these x-rays penetrate their targets to varying degrees and are then reflected onto photographic plates. If the target material is polycrystalline—as are most natural substances—a pattern of rings, like growth rings in the trunk of a tree, is registered on the plates. By the brightness of these rings and by the spacings between them, scientists can determine precisely what the target material is and whether more than one element is present. In fact, such diffraction rings are the fingerprints of matter.

On the other hand, if instead of rings, there is a geometric pattern of white dots on the plate—such as appears in photographs of star fields—then the material is a single crystal, such as diamond or quartz. Patterns of this kind are also distinctive for each element and, accordingly, can be used to discern and identify each. Thus, x-ray diffractometry provides a reliable means for determining the composition as well as the structure of a material.

A very different machine that derives its utility from the use of photon beams is the *emission spectrograph*—a 16-foot-long chamber in which light from an incandescent specimen ricochets off a series of precisely aligned mirrors onto a diffraction grating scored with incredibly fine lines, 15,000 to the inch. These lines break up the light into its various wavelengths and reflect them onto photographic film, where they are recorded as a strip of bright vertical lines separated by dark spaces. Since each element emits a combination of wavelengths peculiar to itself alone, it is possible with emission spectroscopy, to ascertain the composition of any material to a high degree of accuracy. In fact, one foreign atom among a million others can be seen and identified this way.

The subtlest of the photon-beam machines—dependent on a technique only known since 1947—is probably the *electron-spin-resonance* instrument. Here is a device that reaches into metals and many organic compounds to ascertain if they contain free electrons—those not involved in holding the material together. Such materials make good masers for detecting and amplifying weak radio signals coming in from space probes millions of miles away.

In the electron-spin-resonance machine, a material for study is placed in a microwave cavity and subjected to a magnetic field. Free electrons in the sample are captured by the field and compelled to orbit around its lines of force. A microwave signal at right angles to the field is then transmitted to the cavity and through the sample. Now, the magnetic field is deliberately varied in strength until any free electrons in the sample are made not only to rotate around its lines of force but to do so at the same frequency as that of the microwave signal. When this state is reached, such electrons absorb energy from the microwaves and tip over in their orbits, causing a loss of power to occur in the microwave signal that is easily detected by a microwave receiver. Data so obtained provide a wealth of information on the nuclear spin of atoms in the material, the bonding strength between them, the force and direction of electric fields that may exist inside, and the behavior of excited electrons in such an environment.

Easily the most awesome—from the point of view of size and noise—of this family of electronic griffins is the *arc-image*

James Whittaker makes precise adjustments to the diffraction grating in an emission spectrograph.

furnace. A carbon arc of blinding intensity is generated and focused through a chain of concave mirrors to a needle point placed in a vertical shaft into which falls a steady snow of crystalline powder. As this powder reaches the focal point of the mirrors, it is melted instantly and solidifies into a molten mass that grows in size as the powder continues to fall. Strange and beautiful single crystals of materials with very high melting points are produced in such a machine for potential use in lasers and other exotic devices.

Turning to machines that use beams of ions—atoms with a positive charge caused by the loss of one or more electrons—undoubtedly the most impressive is the *mass spectrograph*. Here is a power-packed machine that blasts atoms from a solid sample with a 50,000-volt electric spark, ionizes them, and sends them packing down an S-shaped path across an intense magnetic field that segregates them, according to weight, to crash, like spent bullets into a photographic plate. The vertical line patterns thus created in the photographic emulsion are a clue to the composition of the sample. So sensitive is this technique that one foreign atom among a billion others is easily descried. Such small impurity concentrations are often the ruin of transistors until they are detected and rooted out.

With the attainment of controlled atomic fission during World War II, a wholly new breed of electronic machines for research grew up based upon the particles and electromagnetic energies emanating from the hot interiors of nuclear reactors. At the Rutgers University Reactor Laboratories in Plainsboro, New Jersey, for example, a 5-million-watt swimming pool reactor is used daily by scientists to siphon off beams of slow neutrons and penetrating gamma rays to study the magnetic

Ronald Hand guides the cover of a Van de Graaff
accelerator back into place around the
torpedolike structure which generates the
high-speed electrons produced by the machine.

structure of atomic matter, to induce crystal damage, and to catalyze unusual chemical reactions. Exploiting this latter capability, RCA succeeded a few years ago in building the first laser that could be activated solely by energy from the sun.

The *pièce de résistance* of electronic machinery for research, however, is the computer—a machine, at last, that analyzes, correlates, and in some cases, interprets automatically the rising torrent of complex data spilling from other analytical machines in an ever-widening flood. Already, it is being used to analyze and print out results obtained with mass spectrographs and x-ray diffractometers in many of the nation's laboratories. As a result, work that used to take four to six hours of laborious human analysis is being done by machine in fifteen minutes, with more efficiency and greater economy.

If this were all, it would be enough. However, the real promise of the computer in research lies in its extraordinary capacity for mime—its ability to simulate real events and atomic architecture mathematically. The postulation of mathematical models that attempt to describe or explain what has occurred in an experiment has always been one of the most powerful techniques of the scientific method. Proof or disproof of such models, however, often requires years during which there is great uncertainty and delay. With computers, it is expected these delays will be drastically reduced, if not eliminated. Also, the models they produce should be more accurate since computers can digest far more data, far more quickly.

Such are the wondrous machines of science with which the materials meteorologists of today are charting the electron clouds and photon showers, the magnetic winds and molecular pressure fronts that shape the turbulent atmospheres of the solid state. Manned by crews of dedicated crystallographers, microscopists, spectroscopists, and mathematicians, these machines are powering man through the surface barriers of atomic matter toward the conquest of inner space.

Leslie Burns thrusts out with an experimental superconductive memory plane that can store 16,384 bits of computer information in an area 4 by 4 inches including addressing circuitry.

CHAPTER 8

The Electronic Memory

Asked to describe a modern library, one would probably say it is a building consisting of a librarian, a place to store books, and a card index using numbers and letters to specify each book's location. Ask the same question of an electronic memory engineer, however, and he might well say it is a book-organized, random-access, title-addressable memory system employing an alphanumeric code and a human sense-winding.

Baffling as the second definition may sound, it says precisely the same thing as the first but does so in an extraordinary jargon that has grown up around one of the electronic industry's most astonishing achievements—the *electronic memory*.

Fundamental to all electronic digital computers, this mne-
monic robot is being relied upon increasingly by government
and industry to keep track of such things as payrolls, social
security lists, product inventories, airline reservations, insur-
ance tables, space satellites, and a host of other items. Indeed,
it has become so versatile in recent years that some people
predict its descendants may one day be used to store the entire
spectrum of human knowledge.

Conceived in the early 1940s, electronic memories have been
a major focus of electronics research and development ever
since. In the intervening years such pioneering achievements
as the *Selectron* and the *Myriabit Memory*, both developed by
Dr. Jan A. Rajchman, of RCA Laboratories, have contributed
importantly to their present form and performance.

More recently, in still another significant advance, Dr.
Rajchman's computer research laboratory has developed a
semiconductive memory employing integrated arrays of field-
effect transistors that can process ten million bits of information per second. Such memories are expected to usher in a new
generation of digital computers—faster, smaller, and capable of
greater work loads per work period than ever before.

Integrated transistor arrays are only one form of high-speed
electronic memory under development, however. Others being
perfected by the industry include types that depend for their
operation on such strange and subtle phenomena as holography, magnetic anisotropy, the interaction of electrons with
acoustic waves, and superconductivity.

Although seemingly among the most sophisticated, intricate,
and hopelessly complicated apparatus ever invented, in concept and principle electronic memories are among the simplest.
Like a library, they consist of three essential parts: an area to
store information, a means for putting it in or taking it out,
and an indexing system for locating each separate item. This
last, or indexing system, differs from that of a library only in

using a binary instead of a number-and-letter code. Thus, all information put into an electronic memory is first converted to a language whose alphabet consists of two letters only—negative and positive voltages—and whose words are arbitrary combinations of these "letters."

To appreciate how much information such an indexing system can handle, consider one of the world's best known binary systems—Morse code. With an alphabet of only two letters—dot and dash—enough combinations can be made (twenty-six) to transmit every thought and word in the English language. The same holds true for the binary system of electronic memories.

For binary storage, electronic memories contain a multitude of independent elements, or memory cells, which are capable of storing plus or minus voltages or their magnetic equivalent. (Since electric currents always come with associated magnetic fields, it is possible to use either the electric or magnetic component for storage.)

"Writing" binary information into the memory is made possible by stationing each cell at, near, or around the intersection of a horizontal and a vertical wire or other electrical conductor. Since many cells are involved, the many wires needed are laid out in the form of a grid with a cell at each intersection in the grid. The resulting assembly is called a *memory plane*. In today's standard computer, several planes are usually wired together to form a *memory stack*.

Writing itself is accomplished by picking one horizontal and one vertical wire and sending a unit of electric current down each. In this way, any one—and only one—of the memory cells can be made to intercept both units. Since interception of both is the sole condition on which a cell will store a plus or minus charge (or magnetic field), any cell or sequence of cells can be set as desired.

To read them out, the same vertical and horizontal lines

are used, but this time the two units of current are of opposite sign to those that did the writing. When they converge on the selected cell, therefore, they switch its charge or magnetic field to the opposite sign. As this happens, electromagnetic forces caused by the switching induce a voltage in a nearby wire, termed the *sense-winding*, which carries it outside the memory. With cells in other planes of the memory stack undergoing a similar process simultaneously, the output of the memory, as a whole, is a series of positive and negative voltages which eventually reach such peripheral equipment as an electronic typewriter. Here, they are converted instantly, in accordance with the binary code being used, to everyday English.

Although some experiments using arrays of electrical relays in "on" and "off" positions to store binary information were conducted in the early 1930s, the real history of electronic memories—and computers—begins in 1939 with a little-known visit paid to RCA by representatives from the Frankford Arsenal in Philadelphia. Disturbed by the outbreak in Europe of what later became World War II, and alarmed at the speed and maneuverability of the German Luftwaffe, as demonstrated in its blitzkrieg of Poland, these representatives wanted RCA to develop an electronic fire-control system for antiaircraft guns to replace the slow and cumbersome mechanical "directors" then in use.

After considerable study of the question, including an exhaustive canvass of the technical literature, Dr. Rajchman and his associates agreed to undertake the assignment. Subsequently, their work took two separate directions.

The first derived from the fact that a mathematical relationship exists between the vertical and horizontal angles of a gun and the flight time of its shell, insofar as hitting a target is concerned. Since this relationship is fixed and can be written down as a mathematical table, Dr. Rajchman set out to build an electrical analog of such a table. The outcome was the

Experimental semiconductive, laminated ferrite, superconductive, and sonic-film memories and their supporting components are displayed on a standard chessboard whose organization is very much like their own.

resistive matrix arbitrary function generator, a plate with horizontal conductive lines on one side, vertical lines on the other, and holes containing tiny electrical resistors wherever these lines crossed. Despite its name, this novel device was what we would now call a *read-only* memory—the first ever built.

The second direction led to the development of electronic devices that could perform mathematics. For the resistive matrix to do its job, something had to tell it how high the aircraft was, how fast it was flying, and how soon the anti-aircraft shell would explode after firing. This could only be done by rapid calculations made from data provided by the gun crew. For these calculations a whole new family of electronic counters, multipliers, shift registers, and the like was invented.

As the number and variety of these increased, however, so did the number of vacuum tubes they used. Fearing a trend toward overcomplexity, Dr. Rajchman conceived the idea of a single, integrated tube that could add, subtract, multiply, and divide electronically. Later, he actually designed such a tube—dubbed the *Computron*—and recommended its joint use with the resistive matrix to produce the fire-control system desired.

This idea was especially intriguing to the U.S. Army, which was then fully engaged in World War II and was having serious difficulty providing ballistic tables for its field artillery in advance of actual use. The Computron needed extensive development, however, and RCA, already heavily engaged in the United States war effort and convinced that the proposed fire-control system would prove far too complicated to achieve in time, turned the suggestion down.

A request was then made to the University of Pennsylvania whose Moore School of Electrical Engineering was also involved in research on machine computation. The University accepted and, during the next few years, under the guidance of Dr. J. Presper Eckert and Dr. John Mauchley, with Dr. Rajchman as an early consultant, proceeded to build ENIAC, the world's first electronic digital computer. The year was 1946.

Although ENIAC used individual tubes for its arithmetical functions, it did use resistive matrices for its memory. In so doing, it showed clearly their major limitation as memory devices: the information they contained could not be altered.

ENIAC also incorporated another form of memory device—an electrical "patch-board" for telling the computer how to process the information it stored. Something like a telephone switchboard, it could be used by an operator to wire in an electrical model of the problem to be solved plus instructions on how to solve it. Analog computers still employ such patch-boards for programming even today.

The next big advance in memories, also recorded at the

Dr. Jan Rajchman compares an early electron-tube memory for computers with his latest experimental superconductive memory plane.

Moore School of Electrical Engineering, came in a computer named EDVAC. For information storage, EDVAC used a mercury delay line—a narrow pool of mercury with piezo-electric crystals at either end. Such crystals have an ability to convert sound waves to electricity or vice versa. When an electric current bearing binary information was sent into one of these crystals, it was converted to an acoustic wave which propagated through the mercury, only to be converted back to electric pulses by the crystal at the other end and returned to begin the cycle all over again. Thus, an electroacoustic train of binary pulses was trapped in the circuit and could serve as a memory.

Up to a thousand bits of information could be stored in this way, but there was one serious drawback. EDVAC's memory was a "serial," or phonograph record, sort of device. It was impossible to pick out any single bit of information without reading all that went before it. Though the user might wish to detect only one of the pulses in the train, he had to let all those in front of it pass first. What was to become the perennial memory problem of storage capacity versus access time was highlighted for the first time.

Here matters rested temporarily, while scientists and engineers pondered what next step to take. The answer came soon enough in a far-reaching proposal put forward by Dr. John Von Neumann, of the Institute for Advanced Study in Princeton.

A world-renowned physicist and mathematician, Dr. Von Neumann had been following computer developments with keen interest. He felt their potential was something beyond mere weapons control, and in the light of what had already been accomplished, he formulated the revolutionary concept of a universal computer—one that could solve any problem. Crucial to this concept, he felt, was a memory capable of storing both the data to be processed and the instructions on how to process it. In addition, it seemed such a memory would have to be completely electronic and would have to provide random access to any of its storage elements for both writing and reading. It was not, however, until Dr. Rajchman's demonstration of the *Selectron* in 1948, that a practical, fully digital device for doing this was available.

A vacuum tube containing 256 memory cells pierced by tiny holes and arranged in the form of a grid, the Selectron could produce 256 different electron beams with which to bombard, selectively, any one of these cells. Depending on how the cells were controlled during such bombardment, they could

Dr. Harry L. Pinch places a thin-film permalloy memory
element for computers at the center of a scientific apparatus
for measuring its magnetic fields in three directions.
Permalloy memories work on the principle of magnetic
anisotropy—the ability of some materials to acquire a
magnetic field easily in one direction and with difficulty in
the other. By inducing such fields electrically, it is possible to
store binary information whose meaning is determined by the
direction in which the fields are made to flow.

acquire and retain a negative or positive charge. To read any one of them out, the appropriate electron beam was again used. If the cell was negative, the beam, composed of negative electrons, was repelled. If it was positive, the beam was attracted right through the tiny hole in its center and detected by an electronic device behind it. Therefore, it was possible to determine which cells were negative and which positive and, thereby, to learn what binary information each contained. Such was the first random-access digital memory.

In the months following this historic development, RCA began to manufacture Selectrons at its tube division plant in Lancaster, Pennsylvania, and a computer using a Selectron memory was actually built and operated for several years by the Rand Corporation, the U.S. Air Force–sponsored research organization on the West Coast. The Selectron might well have gone on to become the heart of the modern digital computer had research on it continued, but it was abandoned in the early 1950s following development of the magnetic core.

It had been known for many years that certain metal alloys, such as permalloy, displayed an ability to maintain a magnetic field whose flux lines could be made to point in a clockwise direction or be switched electrically and made to point, with equal facility, in a counterclockwise direction. Thus, the potential for binary storage existed. Nevertheless, these materials were not used because binary storage also required that they support either of two equal and opposite fields and no more. Instead, they supported an uncontrollable number in either direction. In addition, they all took too long to switch. However, considerable research to improve them was done during the war, and they were now ready for a second look.

Aware of this, Dr. Rajchman obtained some improved permalloy and had it formed into small spool-shaped memory cells, which he built into a wire grid as described earlier. Needless to say, they worked and established, beyond doubt, the feasibility of magnetic memories for computers. Even so, Dr. Rajchman was not fully satisfied. Permalloy was too expensive, and it still switched too slowly. What was needed was a cheaper, faster material. Shortly thereafter, such a material was forthcoming in a special kind of *ferrite*—a man-made substance newly developed in the laboratories.

Combining several metal oxides and traces of other elements, ferrites had been under intensive investigation in the electronics industry for use in communications equipment. At this point, however, their potential as a memory material seemed even more compelling to men such as Dr. Rajchman and Jay W. Forrester, of MIT. Both independently enlisted several colleagues doing materials research to prepare special batches, and both developed successful ferrite core memories. In the case of Dr. Rajchman, he used the new material to hand fashion several hundred tiny "doughnuts," or cores, which worked so well that, later, he had several thousand made and proceeded to build the Myriabit Memory, a device capable of storing 10,000 bits of information at one time.

As a result of this work and the decade of research that preceded it, RCA was picked by the U.S. Army Ordnance Department to build a huge digital computer to keep tabs on its entire matériel inventory, from GI boots to tank treads. Using tubes for arithmetic and ferrite cores for memory, this behemoth, known as *Bizmac,* was delivered in 1956 and continued in service for many years.

Meanwhile, memory research goes forward. Coming are micromagnetic, cryoelectric, plated wire, semiconductive, and holographic memories that variously store, process, and regurgitate not millions but billions of facts and figures, not in millionths but in ten-billionths of a second. After that, who knows? With capabilities of this magnitude, perhaps electronic memories will finally reach a point where man has nothing left to put in them that's worth remembering.

Nathan Gordon sits in the center of a computer complex used in scientific research.

CHAPTER 9

Toward Machines That Think

Having learned to amplify the power of man's muscles by means of machines, scientists are now trying to amplify man's intelligence the same way.

At MIT, for example, Dr. Marvin L. Minsky presides over a group working on a machine comprising a stationary TV camera eye and a sophisticated mechanical hand. In front of the machine—a computer—is a table with a child's building blocks scattered over it at random. The purpose of the project is to develop a program of instructions which will make it possible for the camera to direct the hand to build a tower out of the blocks, just as a child might do.

In a similar undertaking at Stanford University, Dr. John McCarthy is trying to develop a set of procedures for use by a related "eye-and-hand" machine which would enable it to assemble simple artifacts from printed instructions. He still has much to do, but already the machine is accomplished enough to pour tea—if you hold a cup in front of it.

At Stanford also, Drs. Edward Feigenbaum and Joshua Lederberg are working to develop an *automatic chemist* employing a computer-controlled mass spectrometer. They foresee such a machine being landed on Mars, where it would conduct experiments automatically to determine the composition and molecular structure of that planet's surface.

Still other work of this type presently underway includes projects aimed at the development of computer procedures that will make it possible for machines to reason and to form theories about things, to read English characters even when they are blurred or only partially formed, and to be trained to recognize and respond to any voice, like a faithful dachshund.

Suffusing all these experimental programs is the desire to amplify man's intelligence with machines that can help him absorb, control, and use more effectively the avalanche of information being generated by the muscle-amplifying and communications-amplifying machines that are presently reshaping society. Implicit in all of them is the assumption that machines may one day be able to think.

Is that a reasonable assumption? Probably not, if "think" is meant in the sense of to have feelings, to experience love, hate, pain, and the other emotions. On the other hand, if "think" is meant in the sense of to display intelligence—to choose the best of several alternatives, to do mathematics, and to act logically—there is mounting evidence that the assumption is valid.

The idea of a machine that really thinks is a difficult one to accept not only because of its unfamiliarity but also because of semantics. What is meant by "think"? Do carbon atoms think? Do hydrogen or oxygen atoms think? Most people would say they do not. Yet, it is these very nonthinking atoms, plus others, which constitute the thinking brain. The only way that sense can be made of this is to conclude, along with the experts in machine reasoning and machine intelligence, that it is not the elements of the brain but the way they are organized—the logic of their association, if you will—that accounts for human thought. If that is so, may not machines also be organized to think? Many scientists now believe they may.

As to how man will know when he has finally achieved a thinking machine, the gifted British mathematician Alan Turing suggested, in the early 1930s, a simple routine which he dubbed the *identification game*. To play it, a person is installed in one room, a computer in another, and another person in a third. All are then put in communication via teletype consoles. The object of the game is for the individual in the third room—the interrogator—to determine, by means of questions and answers sent over the teletype, which of the other two is the machine. To help the interrogator, the person in the first room may even lie. If, despite these handicaps, the machine is still able to frame its responses so as to keep the interrogator in doubt, it may be said to think. The ability to play this game is still considered to be the acid test for machine intelligence, even today. No presently available computer could even come close.

Interestingly, the notion that machines might be built to simulate the mentality and even the behavior of human beings may be traced, in the first recorded instance, to René Descartes, the seventeenth-century French philosopher and mathematician. He foresaw the possibility in a short essay entitled "De Homine" in which he called attention to the automatic nature of many of the functions of the lower animals and of man himself.

This observation did not lead anywhere until 1833, when Charles Babbage, Lucasian Professor of Mathematics at Cambridge University, conceived the world's first mechanical digital computer. Called the *analytical engine,* this incredible contraption was to be powered by steam and to employ gears, wheels, ratchets, pulleys, and the like to perform any arithmetical operation whatsoever. Babbage envisaged that it would consist of a "store" (memory) capable of holding 1,000 fifty-digit numbers, a "mill" (logic section) where the computations would be carried out, a device for transferring numbers between the mill and the store, and an input-output mechanism (he even considered using punched cards) for handling data moving to and from the outside world. He estimated the machine would be able to do sixty additions a minute. Unfortunately, the unit was beyond the mechanical skills of his day and could not be completely built, but the idea for it was the first clear indication that a mechanical contrivance capable of simulating the mathematical powers of the human brain could be designed.

Again, there was a long time interval, and then, in 1927, two years after Dr. Vannevar Bush and his associates had built the first large-scale analog computer at MIT, Alan Turing conceived his *universal automaton*—an abstract characterization of what would now be called a digital computer.

Turing described his automaton as consisting of an infinite tape divided into equal squares and passing under a reading head, like the tape in a video recorder. In each square was a symbol (a zero or a one) which the head could read, erase, change, or rewrite in accordance with instructions included on the tape. After performing one of these operations, the head could then move the tape forward or backward to the next square.

Turing proceeded to prove mathematically that such a machine, so organized, could imitate, if instructed to do so, any other automaton. This is what made it universal. It could even reproduce itself, he concluded. In postulating such a machine, Turing was the first to enunciate clearly the need both for problem description (data) and for instructions (programs) in order to operate a computer.

Nineteen years later, in 1946, John Von Neumann conceived his idea of using a stored program in the computer memory in order to realize the computer's potential as an intellectual automaton. His idea came too late for ENIAC, which processed data according to the way its circuits were wired together. The first stored-program computer was, instead, the Electronic Delay Storage Automatic Calculator (EDSAC, for short) built at the mathematical laboratory of Cambridge University in 1949.

Von Neumann was also one of the earliest to propose use of the binary number system as the language of digital computers on the ground that, with its exclusive reliance on 1s and 0s, it paralleled symbolically the on-off nature of the electronic switches that make up such machines.

Independent of these efforts to build intellectual automata and make them work, Dr. Warren McCulloch, then of the University of Illinois, and Dr. Walter Pitts, of MIT, collaborated on the development of a theory, published in 1943, in which they proved that any concept or idea capable of being put completely and unambiguously into words could be realized as well in a finite network of digital units with the following properties: each could be excited to give an output or be inhibited from doing so; the output of one would act as a stimulus for another; each would give an output only when a certain threshold was reached; and each would exhibit the same time delay after being fired and before it could be fired again. What they were describing was the human nervous system and what they had proved was that this nervous system is really an automaton, not unlike a computer, composed of tiny "black boxes" (neurons) linked in networks whose operation follows logical principles. The concept of a black box encompasses any unit whose internal structure is not known but which accepts inputs and gives outputs. In this sense, even a car engine is a black box to anyone but a garage mechanic, and so is a TV set to anyone but a television engineer.

What they meant by logical principles was that such networks operate as if they have an AND function (this and this, expressing conjunction), an OR function (this or this, expressing disjunction), and a NO function (this not this, expressing negation). With these three functions, it turns out, a complete set of logical operations can be performed, from which a set of procedures can be developed for detecting a criminal in the best Sherlock Holmes tradition or for solving for x in a high school algebra problem. All other logical operations, no matter how complex, can be derived from these.

Thus, by 1950, the theory and the fact of automata had reached the point where sophisticated electronic digital computers could be built to ape some of the functions of the human brain, and the brain itself, through studies of the nervous system, had been reduced to the status of little more than an incredibly complex automaton. The conclusion was inescapable. If the mind is such an automaton, then it should be able to reproduce itself by other than biological methods.

It is this conclusion, more than any other, which accounts for the undercurrent of excitement that permeates the ranks of the mathematicians and logicians, the physicists and engineers, the neurologists and psychologists who are in the van of research in this field. They know there is no theoretical reason why artificial intelligence should not be able to exist. Indeed, the evidence is all the other way. All that is needed is time, an improved grasp of logical processes, a deeper under-

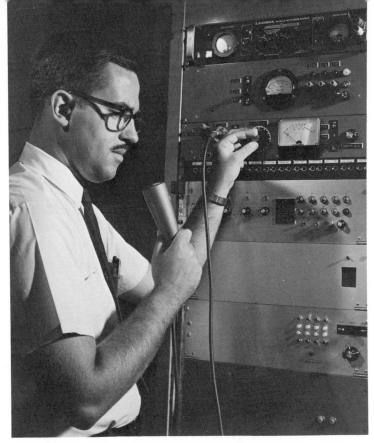

Dr. Paul Ross works with a computer that can be trained to recognize his voice and the simple commands he speaks.

standing of the mental procedures used to solve problems, a better exegesis of the theory and operation of neurons and neural networks, and further progress in developing electronic components, from which memory and logic circuits of sufficient reliability, complexity, and low power consumption can be assembled, to produce an ersatz mind.

The value of such machines, when achieved, can only be surmised, but it ought to be tremendous. They would make possible automatic planes that avoid midair collisions on their own; cars that never have accidents; production machinery that understands the nature of the product it is making and that even makes suggestions on how to improve it; robots that can explore the ocean floor and develop theories about its evolution; automatic spacecraft that can scout star systems and unknown planets in deep space too far away for a useful communications link to be maintained with earth; vast cities whose complex transportation, communications, supply, and control functions are part of a machine intelligence which monitors and supports them. Such are some of the giddy prospects in store for our civilization if we succeed in building machine intelligence into the increasingly artificial environment to which our mechanical, electronic, and nuclear sciences are giving birth.

Even if such dazzling possibilities were never to be realized, however, the effort to achieve machine intelligence would still be worthwhile. Already, as a result of it, a great deal has been learned about how the body and mind function, a must if further progress in medicine and surgery is to be made. Also, it has produced the modern digital computer which is rapidly finding application in every sort of activity, from record keeping in business and industry to the monitoring of industrial processes, the launching and guidance of space vehicles, the control of vehicular and communications traffic, and the quest for greater scientific knowledge of ourselves and our environment.

This is only the beginning, however. Machines endowed with far more than a mere ability to process data in accordance with instructions painstakingly prepared by human programmers are definitely on the horizon. When they arrive, they will show an ability to collect their own data, to write and modify programs which they themselves have generated, and to recommend or take direct action, depending on what peripheral gear is associated with them. They will be faster, more efficient, more clever, and more versatile than anything we have yet built.

Finally, such machines will be fun. At last, man will have something in his environment, other than his fellow men, with which he can strike up an intellectual camaraderie, from which he can learn, and to which he can resort for help in solving problems beyond his ken.

Magnetic domains in a garnet crystal show up as camouflage markings in polarized light. A pattern of iron filings is superimposed on crystal to suggest its magnetic properties.

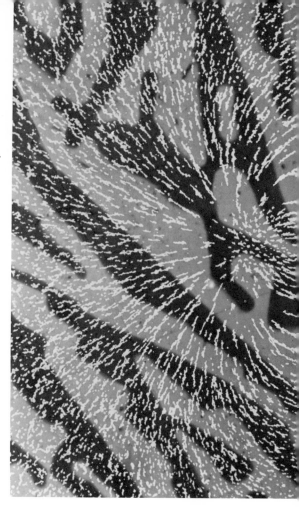

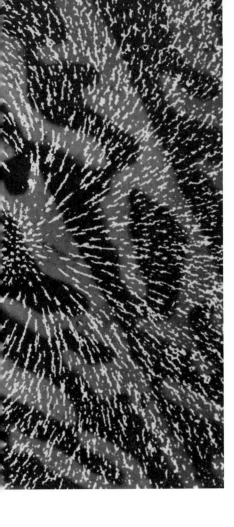

_____

CHAPTER 10

The
Magnetic
Personality
of Matter

They sound like the crowd at a rummage sale. Their conversation is larded with enthusiastic references to bottles, mirrors, tapes, saws, loudspeakers, cores, yokes, door fasteners, and a mélange of other seemingly drab and half-forgotten clutter to be found in any well-seasoned attic or basement. Actually, though, they are specialists in the arcane and newly awakened field of magnetics—a field whose growth and diversification recently has propelled it into the vanguard of modern electronics research.

The "bottles" and "mirrors" are not physical objects but magnetic fields so powerful they will contain the hot electron-

103

proton plasmas currently being used by scientists in their effort to achieve controlled thermonuclear fusion. If they succeed, man will have a new and virtually inexhaustible energy source at his command.

The tapes are also magnetic—iron oxides bound in synthetic resins and gathered on stubby reels. Stored on them are the color and black-and-white images of much of current television programming, the symphonies and chorales of modern stereophonic sound systems, the staccato 1s and 0s of slick new computers and data-processing equipment.

The "saws" are a new wrinkle—pulsed magnetic fields so intense they literally drive atoms from the materials set before them, leaving ragged fissures behind, much as a saw would do.

Loudspeakers for reproducing sound, ferrite cores for storing information in the memories of digital computers, ferrite yokes for guiding the electron beams that sketch the pictures on your television screen, the Alnico fasteners that pull your cupboard door shut—these too are magnetic. So are key parts of the doorbell and the telephone, the electric motor and the dynamo, the radio and the electron microscope. Everywhere, in fact, magnetism and magnetic devices are steadily infiltrating and enriching our lives.

There are two principal reasons for this. First, the success of modern atomic theory in explaining the sources and consequences of magnetism in matter has given us the means to produce and apply this protean phenomenon in a growing variety of ways.

Second, due to the little-known labors of Jacob L. Snoek and a team of Dutch scientists, who managed in the early 1940s to conduct a series of seminal investigations into the nature and magnetic behavior of ferrites—despite the Nazi occupation of Holland—we now have a chemistry that enables us to produce a class of substances whose magnetic properties are almost completely controllable.

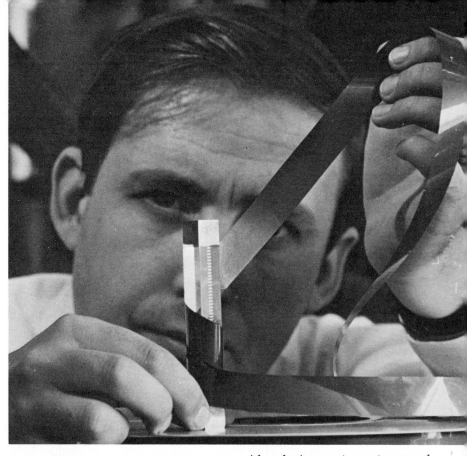

A length of magnetic tape is wrapped around an experimental sonic-film memory which might one day replace it. Dr. Lubemyr Ohyshkevych is shown in background.

Matthew Orlando pulls a coil of magnetic tape symbolically from a collander of black ferrite powder which gives the tape its magnetic storage properties.

Not that magnetism was unknown or unused until this time. Recognition of its existence goes back at least 3,000 years to ancient China and to the vanished kingdom of Magnesia, formerly in Asia Minor, from whose name the term "magnetism" is probably derived.

The first known instrument to employ magnetism—the compass—was in use by navigators on the China Sea in the eleventh century and, on the other side of the world, was first described by the French crusader Peter Peregrinus de Maricourt in 1269. De Maricourt also fathered the concept of magnetic poles.

Much later, in 1600, Sir William Gilbert, physician to Queen Elizabeth I, published a famous treatise on magnetism in which he suggested, for the first time, that the earth itself is a huge bar magnet.

In short, the magnetic effects of attraction, repulsion, and orientation (the compass) were well known and in limited use by the end of the sixteenth century. None of this helped explain what magnetism is or how it is produced, however. Even the discovery by Michael Faraday and Joseph Henry, in 1831, of electromagnetic induction—the principle by which a varying magnetic field can be made to initiate an electric current in a conductor, or vice versa—only succeeded in producing still another, albeit profoundly valuable, effect.

It is only in the past 100 years, with the recognition of the electromagnetic nature of light, the formulation of modern atomic theory, the discovery of the electron, and the development of quantum mechanics that we have begun to unravel the mystery.

It turns out that magnetism is as fundamental to the fabric of the universe as the quantities of mass, electric charge, and gravitation. All the basic building blocks of matter—the electron, the proton, and the neutron—have magnetic poles and join magnetically (as well as other ways) to form the atomic elements, from hydrogen to uranium and above. In doing so, furthermore, they usually join with the north pole of one opposite the south pole of the other in an inverted or *antiferromagnetic* posture which causes their tiny magnetic fields or "magnetic moments" to cancel completely. Virtually all atomic matter is bound this way, as is all molecular matter including that composing plants, animals, and man himself.

The reason for the "anti" designation is that a handful of metallic elements—iron, nickel, cobalt, and the rare earths dysprosium and gadolinium—were the first materials to be classified according to their magnetic properties and their atoms all turned out to be exceptions to the above rule; that is, they combine *ferromagnetically* with north pole opposite north pole and south pole opposite south pole. Thus, instead of canceling, their magnetic moments add together cumulatively. Although few in number, it is these materials, or combinations of them, that make the strongest magnets. For a long time, they were the only materials thought to display magnetic behavior.

In the early 1930s, however, a new class of magnetically active materials, called *ferrites,* came under investigation at the research laboratories of the Philips Gloeilampenfabrieken in Holland, one of the world's largest electronics companies. It was as part of this effort that Snoek and his coworkers made their momentous findings during World War II.

Ferrites are ferrimagnetic substances. That is, they contain several atoms of unequal magnetism coupled *antiferromagnetically* in a distinctive pattern—called a *spinel structure—* which repeats itself over and over as the volume of the material grows, just as the metal links that make up a piece of chain mail repeat. Since the magnetic atoms of such patterns, or "links," do not completely cancel, due to their uneven magnetism, the links have a net moment and so, therefore, does the material as a whole.

Without qualification, it is these and similar materials—iron oxide compounds, in general—that have kindled today's much-publicized electronics revolution. Lacking them, the development of television, computer memories, audio and video tape, radar, and vhf, uhf, and microwave radio communications would have been greatly hampered, if not prevented.

There are several reasons for this. For one, ferrites are electrical insulators. They can be used to sense and process radio waves oscillating at up to 100 million cycles per second without sustaining the prohibitive electrical losses associated with the only other materials that have been tried in this job—the ferromagnetic metals. For another, even in bulk form, their north and south poles can be reversed easily and completely by the application of very small outside magnetic fields. This is what

Dr. Peter Wojtowicz is shown explaining a molecular model of a spinel structure. Formulas used in magnetic equations are written on blackboard in background.

gives them the ability to store and process computer information in binary form.

In microscopic, needlelike particles, too, ferrites can be frozen into plastic binders where they will still respond magnetically to the application of an outside field by altering the direction of their internal fields. This is the basis for their use in magnetic tapes.

In yet another form, they make good permanent magnets, light enough to hold papers or other items to an upright metal surface without falling of their own weight. Also, because ferrites are really ceramics and are derived from abundant materials in the earth's surface, they are extremely cheap to manufacture.

The differences between *ferro-* and *ferri*magnetism are not basic but originate in the divergent atomic mechanisms by which each is produced. All atomic magnetism arises from the existence, in certain atomic orbits, of electrons whose inherent magnetism is not canceled by antiferromagnetic coupling to other electrons. There are approximately twenty-five elements in nature whose atoms incorporate such unpaired electrons. Since none of these atoms is able to neutralize its magnetism, or magnetic moment, internally, for reasons implicit in the quantum-mechanical building codes which govern their fabrication, they attempt to do so by going outside.

The ferromagnets are crystals built from atoms of equal magnetism assembled into tiny magnetic cadres or "domains," like soldiers in a parade square. Since all the members of the domain "face" in the same direction, magnetically speaking, their moments add together to give the domain a cumulative moment. Like a parade square, too, such a domain cannot keep adding atomic "soldiers" forever. Eventually, it reaches an optimum size, stops growing, and a new one is started. The members of the new one will all face in a different direction, however, and those of the next in yet another until, as a result, all domain moments counterbalance and effectively cancel each other. Thus, iron, fresh from the mine, seems nonmagnetic.

Ferrimagnets, on the other hand, are crystals built from atoms of unequal magnetism assembled into domains in an antiferromagnetic pattern—again like a parade square, but this time with columns of atomic soldiers facing alternately front, rear, front, rear. Ordinarily, this arrangement would cause all atomic moments to cancel. However, those columns facing front have greater magnetism than those facing to the rear, so a net moment for each domain develops. To neutralize such moments, ferrimagnetic materials, such as ferrites, arrange to balance off their domains against each other, just as the ferro-magnets do.

The instant either ferromagnets or ferrimagnets are subjected to an outside magnetic field, though, the magnetic moments of all their domains fall immediately into line and their true magnetic character manifests itself by the appearance of a collective moment for the material as a whole. When the outside field is removed, however, the domains reassert their independence, and this collective moment begins gradually to decline.

There are many more forms of magnetism, of course: *nuclear magnetism,* which has led to such devices as proton magnetometers used by archaeologists to detect the presence of buried civilizations; *paramagnetism,* a dilute kind of ferromagnetism which has been used to help cool materials to within a few thousandths of a degree of absolute zero; *metamagnetism,* exhibited by a few substances which are antiferromagnetic at one temperature and ferromagnetic at another; *diamagnetism,* which derives from the orbital motion of the electron and not its internal structure; and *electromagnetism,* which is created by the flow of electrons in a conductor or superconductor. But, for the electronics scientist, it is ferrimagnetism that holds the greatest fascination.

Hans Lehmann demonstrates that a polycrystalline slug of cadmium-chromium-selenide becomes ferromagnetic at liquid nitrogen temperatures. The frosted beaker is sitting in a small electromagnet which has induced a field in the slug to which ordinary stick pins cling tenaciously.

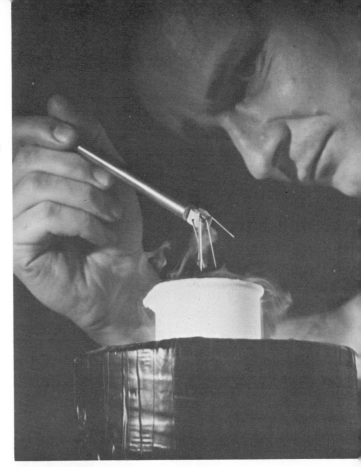

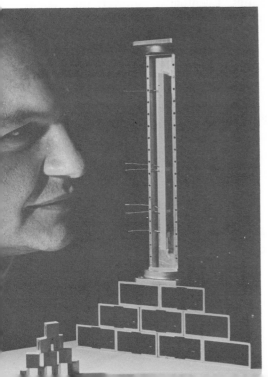

Scientist W. Siekanowicz looks at an open waveguide with a center rail composed of ferrite "toroids" similar to those stacked in the foreground, left. When fully assembled and integrated, these various elements will form a new kind of radar system whose microwave beams can be steered back and forth across the sky electronically instead of mechanically, as is presently done.

This preference springs largely from the fact that in ferri-magnetism several different atoms, arranged in a distinct and repeating pattern, are involved. Therefore, it is possible chemically to shift them around within the pattern, to substitute other atoms for them, to isolate them one from another, and in a word, to tailor the magnetism of the pattern with remarkable precision.

Because of such finger-tip control, the electronics industry has been able to devise some wondrous ferrites for use in television yokes, radio and radar systems, and computer memories. In fact, new families of *lithium ferrites* for computer memories, *barium ferrites* for audio loudspeakers, *manganese ferrites* for use in phased-array radar systems, and still other varieties for application in magnetic tape have been developed recently and promise to advance these fields dramatically in the years ahead.

Recently, also, from knowledge gained in painstaking studies of ferrites, the industry has succeeded in developing an astonishing new class of materials that are true ferromagnets, though they will not conduct electricity. At present, they operate only at very low temperatures. Eventually, however, they might well provide the basis for a clutch of new electronic components including magnetically activated transistors, diodes, oscillators, and some radically different devices such as *spin wave* amplifiers for boosting radio, microwave, and even millimeter wave transmissions.

Spin waves are generated in certain materials by electromagnetic waves. They result from the field of one magnetic atom being pushed by the magnetic component of an incoming radio wave. This push is passed on immediately to the next magnetic atom and so on down the line, like a pail of water being handed along a bucket brigade. Thus, the energy of a radio wave oscillating in space can be transformed into a magnetic disturbance propagating through a solid. In this latter form, it is believed, such energy should be subject to amplification by a number of sophisticated techniques.

From curiosity to compass to computer memory, magnetism has moved irresistibly through the centuries, from the periphery of human affairs to the center of some of our subtlest scientific and finest technological achievements.

X marks the spot on the bottle-shaped quartz crystal held in tweezers where a superconductive tunnel diode detects phonons at a frequency of 70 Gigahertz. Dr. Yehuda Goldstein prepares to insert the experimental device into a microwave cavity while liquid nitrogen fumes from the cryogenic dewar below.

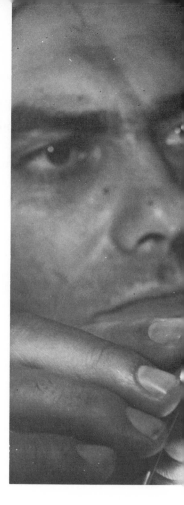

CHAPTER 11

The
Sonic
Electron

A cache of new and unusual electronic effects, based on the interactions that occur between electrons and sound waves propagating through solids, has been uncovered and may soon be exploited by the nation's enterprising electronics industry.

New products expected to result from this find include: acoustoelectric oscillators, detectors, mixers, and amplifiers that may spawn a new breed of radio communications equipment; acoustoelectric computer memories that may store 50 million bits of information on a handful of quartz rods; solid-state microwave transmitters and receivers that do away with the bulky waveguides, hot electron tubes, and clumsy coaxial

115

cables that bedizen modern radar and television installations; sonic masers that generate sound waves so intense they may cut or pulverize metals; and acoustoelectric photomultipliers that may one day employ sound to amplify light.

At the very least, it appears, mastery of these acoustoelectric interactions can be used to improve the quality and perform- ance of present electronic materials and devices. These exciting possibilities stem from the fact that, when an electric field is applied to a hunk of solid matter, free electrons, floating aim- lessly therein, begin to drift purposefully down-field at a rate fixed by the pressure of the field (voltage) and by the drag exerted by the atom sea around them (resistance). This drag, arising from tiny vibrations of the atoms in the solid, is really a manifestation of sound energy oscillating constantly through the material at frequencies too high to be heard.

Ordinarily, such vibrations are a nuisance in electronic cir- cuits because they cause heating and electrical resistance in various components. Recently, however, scientists have dis- covered that in semiconductors, such as cadmium sulfide, and in superconductors, such as niobium tin, these ultrasonic vibra- tions control the behavior of free electrons adrift inside in a number of surprising and potentially useful ways.

In cadmium sulfide, for example, they may form an in- visible sound barrier which effectively limits the speed of elec- trons moving through the material to the speed of sound. The phenomenon is reminiscent of that encountered by the aircraft industry twenty years ago when its airplanes were temporarily denied higher speeds by the sound barrier in the atmosphere.

There are significant differences, however. Whereas the atmospheric sound barrier was viewed as an obstacle to progress by aircraft manufacturers, its counterpart in solids, together with other acoustoelectric phenomena, is viewed by electronics manufacturers as a new source of ways to amplify, switch, and otherwise control electric currents.

A portion of what lies in store has already been realized through the phenomenon of superconductivity—one form of acoustoelectric effect produced in certain metals when they are submerged in frigid baths of liquid helium. This phenomenon has been harnessed successfully to create crushing magnetic fields, to store computer data, and to amplify microwaves and has even been enlisted to track ultrasonic sound waves speeding through certain crystals.

Now, other acoustoelectric effects have been found and used experimentally in materials at normal temperatures to amplify sound directly without transforming it first to electric currents, to tune and modulate the intense light beam of lasers, to stimulate the emission of massive laserlike sound waves from certain crystals, and to probe the atomic structures and energy exchanges that occur in solids generally.

In a superficial sense, of course, acoustics and electronics have been teamed more or less from the inception of the industry. The invention of the microphone, the speaker, and the ultrasonic transducer—and their subsequent application to voice radio, telephone, public address systems, movie sound tracks, stereophonic phonographs, and sonar testify to that. But, this relationship has always had something of a brute-force nature. The sound waves acting on the diaphragm of a microphone or the electromagnetic forces acting on the cone of a speaker trigger sonic vibrations that disturb the whole atomic structure of these devices. In neither do specific acoustic waves interact with specific electrons in any meaningful way. Sound at these frequencies (10 to 20,000 cycles per second) is a bulk phenomenon, like the tides in the ocean.

Even at ultrasonic frequencies up to hundreds of millions of cycles per second, sound is still a bulk phenomenon. But, when its frequencies soar into the billions-of-cycles-per-second range—and especially above 10 billion—its vibrational character acquires a radically new dimension. At these levels, the crests and troughs in the sound waves, vibrating along the atomic networks that make up the solid state, are so tiny and intense that they begin to interact with individual atoms in the networks and even with individual electrons.

In fact, it becomes increasingly difficult to think of these perturbations as sound waves at all. Rather, they begin to assume the character of elementary particles. Accordingly, they have come to be called *phonons* in the same way that light waves are now said to consist of elementary particles called *photons*.

Recognition that such sonic waves or phonons can oscillate at these high frequencies may be traced to the work of Einstein, Peter Debye, and others in the early 1920s. In studies of atomic vibrations in crystals, these men noted that sound waves can have frequencies as high as 100 trillion cycles per second, or the equivalent, in electromagnetic terms, of infrared light.

There was no inkling at this time that the passage of phonons through a material was invariably associated with an electrical disturbance, however. That connection was not made until 1953 when Dr. Robert Parmenter, then at MIT and now at the University of Arizona, jolted scientific circles by suggesting the existence of such a disturbance traveling at the same speed and in the same direction as the sound wave causing it. It resulted, he hypothesized, from tiny electrical imbalances in the atomic structure of the solid occasioned by the bunching and thinning of the atoms in response to the rhythmic undulations of the sound energy. Dubbed the *acoustoelectric effect,* its existence was confirmed in 1959 by Dr. Gabriel Weinreich, of Bell Telephone Laboratories, in the course of experiments on germanium, the raw material of the first transistors.

Two years prior to that, in 1957, the phonon concept came into special prominence when it was cited by Drs. John Bardeen, Leon N. Cooper, and J. Robert Schrieffer, then at the University of Illinois, as the key factor in producing

Roland Smith observes backscatter from the cadmium sulfide
crystal being hit by the beam from a helium-neon laser. He
is attempting to bounce the laser beam from the crests of
phonon waves occurring naturally in the crystal.

superconductivity. According to their theory, now widely accepted, superconductivity occurs when electrons fall to such low energies in a material that they join together and travel in pairs. The force that binds them, despite their strong electrical antipathy, derives from the constant exchange of a phonon between them. In other words, superconductive electrons exist as partners locked in a kind of ultrasonic embrace.

A more concrete demonstration of phonon-electron interaction occurred in 1961 when Drs. Andrew Hutson, James McFee, and David White, also of Bell Telephone Laboratories, directly amplified sound waves in a crystal of cadmium sulfide by applying an electric field to the crystal. What they got, it turned out, was an ultrasonic microphone-amplifier-speaker all in one.

At about the same time, Roland Smith, an experimentalist working at RCA Laboratories, discovered further that the mechanism producing this unusual effect also restricts the velocity of free electrons streaming through the crystal to the speed of sound, whenever their numbers approach a certain critical density. In 1962, a related effect was seen to occur in the semimetal bismuth by Dr. Leo Esaki, of IBM, inventor of the tunnel diode.

As a result of these experiments and the conclusions drawn from them, the following picture has begun to emerge regarding some of the interactions that occur in solids between electrons and phonons. When an electron slides down the voltage ways, so to speak, of an electric circuit and splashes into a solid component, it sends shock waves ahead of it, just as a ship does when it slides into water. The pressure it exerts as it bumps against the atoms composing the device creates phonon waves (ultrasonic vibrations) forward of its "bow" and a well-defined phonon wake astern. These are in addition to the sonic ripples already present in the material naturally due to internal heat.

In certain instances, the bow waves may reinforce and

amplify the sound waves naturally present or some others introduced from outside. In the one case, such amplified waves may be used by scientists to study the physics of the substance or, in the other, to produce the ultrasonic microphone-amplifier-speaker reported by Bell Telephone Laboratories.

With regard to superconductors, it is not the bow waves but the phonon wake that is of interest. What seems to happen is that the two electrons in each superconductive pair whirl around a common center while floating in each other's wake. They achieve their whirling motion by "surfing" on these wakes, like Hawaiian surfboard riders scudding along the brow of a rolling surge.

Though intensive investigation of the sound waves known as phonons has scarcely begun, research has already uncovered the sonic electron for amplifying them and the supersonic electron twosomes that use them to produce superconductivity. With still more such effects sure to be found, the conclusion seems inescapable that electrons, unlike children, are often better behaved when they are "heard" and not seen.

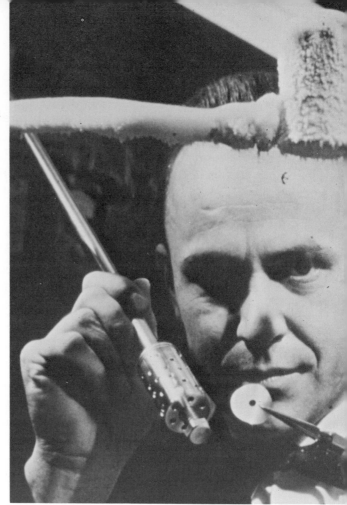

Dr. Joseph Hanak in cryogenic environment holds up disk of niobium-tin rings which have been used to trap magnetic fields of up to 50,000 gauss. Dr. Hanak is the developer of a vapor-deposition process which was used to put down rings.

CHAPTER 12

Superconductivity

Dense electric currents 2,500 times thicker than the currents that can be squeezed through a normal copper wire, persistent currents carried without the slightest resistance in supercooled metal films, thinner than steam on a windowpane, structured currents whose orderly flow generates magnetic fields so fierce they can exert 12 tons of pressure per square inch or so facile they can open and close an electric switch 100 million times a second—such are the manifestations of superconductivity.

First observed in 1911 by the Dutch physicist Heike Kamerlingh Onnes superconductivity is presently central to a number of scientific investigations aimed at achieving an exotic generation of high-performance computers, microwave radar and communications equipment, magnets, scientific instruments, high-current storage batteries, magnetohydrodynamic (MHD) power supplies, and propulsion systems for outer space.

Although there is reason to hope that superconductivity may one day be found to exist in some materials at room temperature, for the moment it is a phenomenon of the utterly cold. In most of the 900 metals and metal alloys in which it has been produced, its onset is triggered by cooling to the atom-numbing temperatures of liquid helium—484°F below the freezing point of water and only 7°F above absolute zero!

Precisely what happens to the atomic and electronic organization of metals at such chilling levels is still not wholly

Robert Gange inspects an experimental superconductive memory plane which may one day store 250,000 bits of information as tiny circulating electric currents that never decay so long as the plane remains superconductive.

understood. Nevertheless, great light was shed on the subject in 1957 when University of Illinois scientists John Bardeen, Leon N. Cooper, and J. Robert Schrieffer succeeded in extracting from the rich lodestone of quantum mechanics a theory which explains most of what is observed. Based on this theory (now called the *BCS theory*) and the sharp, if less comprehensive, insights of several other investigators, the following picture of superconductivity can be drawn.

Though ostensibly hard and unyielding, metals are really underwater jungle gyms at the submicroscopic level—rigid networks of atoms submerged in a thick electron "soup." Though their electrons do not really lose individuality, they are so numerous and so intermingled that they take on the appearance of a continuous fluid. Thus, the slightest heat disturbs them, as it does water molecules, not only individually, but collectively. Eddies, waves, and other perturbations appear as bulk phenomena.

These can be completely overridden and a current made to flow, however, if an electric field stronger than the heat energy present is applied. The heat does not disappear, of course. It remains as a source of turbulence in the current. To overcome this turbulence and, therefore, to increase the amount of current metals will carry, scientists usually resort to cooling. This helps greatly but, for most metals, does not eliminate the problem.

There are a few spectacular exceptions, however, such as lead and tin in which cooling steadily reduces turbulence until suddenly—dramatically—near temperatures at which helium condenses to a soft and limpid liquidity, turbulence disappears altogether and huge electric currents begin to flow. It is these which have come to be called superconductors.

What is thought to occur in such materials is that the electrons in their currents drop to an energy level so low they can no longer travel independently. Instead, they form into couples whose members have opposite spins (Cooper pairs) and, synchronizing their action with that of every other couple, move in a series of changing patterns and partners through the superconductor.

Strangely, these whirling partners never touch but glide through the metal bouncing a unit of acoustic energy, called a phonon, back and forth between them, like two basketball players working a ball down court. There is none of the disorder associated with their movement in a normal metal and, therefore, no resistance to their flow. Once started, they will circulate forever, providing the metal is kept supercold.

Some measure of the incredible density of these currents may be gained by realizing that a niobium-tin compound, first produced by Bernd Matthias while at Bell Telephone Laboratories, has been known to carry up to 500,000 amperes of electric current per square centimeter, when superconductive. That compares with a maximum of 200 amperes for normal copper wire, the universal carrier of electric current.

Two significant side effects of these high and persistent electric currents in superconductors are their collective *magnetic moment* and their *inductance*. Their moment is a product of the fact that a magnetic field is generated by an electron as it moves in a conductor. This field always appears perpendicular to the electron's line of flight and, in superconductors, adds to the field of all other electrons to produce a combined field which has been measured, in several instances, to exceed that of the earth by 200,000 times or better.

Their inductance, on the other hand, embodies the idea of the magnetic field of one forward-moving electron acting to oppose the forward acceleration of all other electrons. This everybody-back-me-first attitude gives rise to a form of drag, a kind of inertia which must be neutralized for a net electric current to start flowing or change direction. This effect has already been successfully harnessed to produce a new kind of computer switch and a new kind of microwave amplifier.

Ronald Hughes prepares to lower the world's first microwave superconductive amplifier into a dewar of liquid helium.

Richard Weiss grasps a niobium-tin superconductive magnet capable of generating a field of 100,000 gauss in its central bore.

A final and seemingly paradoxical feature of superconductors is their diamagnetism—their tendency to shield against magnetic fields, including those they themselves generate. Up to a certain point—different for different materials—superconductors will not permit magnetic fields to penetrate them. When such fields attempt to do so, they generate electric currents on the surface of the superconductor. These currents, in turn, create a magnetic field of opposite polarity to the external field and cancel it. In other words, the superconductor fights fire with fire.

If the external field is too strong, however, it induces such powerful surface currents that the superconductor becomes heated and reverts either to a "normal" or to a mysterious "mixed" state. Depending into which state it goes, a superconductor is said to be *type 1* or *type 2*.

In the case of type 1 materials, the transition to the normal state is almost instantaneous, coming when the external field reaches a certain critical strength.

In the case of type 2 materials, the transition to the normal state proceeds very gradually and is marked by a rising number of magnetic lines of force (flux lines) being allowed to penetrate the material without its going normal—at least for a while. What seems to happen is that microscopic flaws in the structure of type 2 superconductors go normal, piecemeal, as the external magnetic field grows. When they do, they form tiny pores through which some lines of force from this field can pass. Instead of causing the whole material to go normal right away, these lines get "pinned" in the flaws for a time and remain isolated from the stream of electron pairs whirling silently around them. If they could be seen, they would give the impression of nails driven through a board. As the number of such flux penetrations mounts, a point is eventually reached when they are so dense that the type 2 superconductor can no longer support them, and it relapses into the completely normal state.

Because of this unusual character, superconductors of the second kind are particularly suited to producing high magnetic fields. Using a material such as a niobium-tin film deposited on a stainless steel ribbon several hundred feet long and coiled on itself like a watch spring, RCA engineers have generated a magnetic field 280,000 times stronger than the earth's in a cylinder 6 inches in diameter.

Efforts to make use of the electron-saturated state of matter, known as superconductivity, did not begin in earnest in the electronics industry until after 1956. In the time since, however, they have multiplied so rapidly and have grown to include such a wide range of potential products that it has even been suggested, facetiously, that the color television set of the future may yet carry a tag advising: *For best results, keep in liquid helium.*

Dr. Samir Ahmed uses a pyrometer to check the temperature of an argon plasma being tested as a means of propulsion for spaceships.

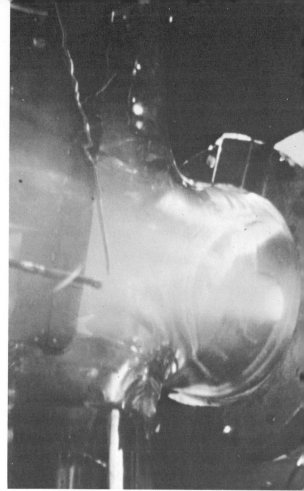

CHAPTER 13

The
Fourth
State
of Matter

On the drawing boards or under development in the nation's bustling research laboratories is a spectacular array of new electronic products whose performance will derive from a strange, fourth state of matter known as *plasma*.

Identified and described by Dr. Lewi Tonks and Dr. Irving Langmuir in 1929, plasmas are now the basis for a gathering scientific upheaval in the fields of direct energy conversion, space propulsion, communications, weaponry, industrial processing, and basic research.

Not solid, not liquid, not gas—plasmas are a kind of electronic "jelly" composed of equal numbers of negatively charged

131

electrons and positively charged ions held together by their own long-range electrical forces. They are generated when the atoms of a stable element, such as mercury, are excited—usually by heat or electrical energy—to a point where their nuclei and some or all of their electrons dissociate.

While they are too energetic to reassemble into atoms, these free electrons and free ions are not energetic enough to escape their mutual electrical attraction and continue to swarm in each other's vicinity. Therefore, they form a seething, vibrating, electronic "funny putty" which is surprisingly stable, cohesive, and electrically neutral.

Though plasmas have some of the character of a gas—they will diffuse to fill any container, for example—they are quite different. They can exist even in solids. Solid-state plasmas are a current focus of intense study at several industrial and university laboratories because of their ability to generate high-frequency radio waves.

Interestingly, plasmas have been an intimate part of our world from the very beginning, although they have moved to the fore of scientific research only recently. The sun is a plasma. Racked by continuous thermonuclear explosions and multimillion-degree temperatures, squeezed by gravitational pressures that would add tons to the weight of a man on its surface, buffeted by fierce electric fields, magnetic storms, and other cosmic disturbances, the sun could not exist as anything *but* a plasma.

The ionosphere, too, is a plasma. Enveloping the earth from an altitude of 60 miles out to several hundred, it makes possible worldwide communications by reflecting shortwave and other radio frequencies back and forth to the ground until they have propagated around the world.

Man-made electron tube devices for converting alternating to direct current, such as thyratrons and ignitrons, also employ plasmas. The mammoth Ballistic Missile Early Warning System (BMEWS) uses ignitrons to produce and shape the powerful radar pulses with which it sweeps the northern skies in search of hostile intruders.

Because of their peculiar structure, plasmas have a wealth of useful properties not found in any other form of matter. For example, they vibrate at a constant frequency that varies with their density. Scientists refer to this as their "natural," or plasma, frequency. Since a vibrating electric charge can emit electromagnetic radiation ranging from radio waves to light, a collection of such charges in a plasma can do the same. For this reason, plasmas are being considered for use in a whole new family of radio communications equipment.

Plasma vibrations can be a mixed blessing, however. Not only do they act as a mechanism by which to generate radio waves, but they can also be used, in a different way, to suppress or reflect them. The fact is that plasmas will not allow a radio wave oscillating at less than their own natural frequency to pass through them. This explains why we lose contact with our manned space capsules at some point during reentry. Their torrid plunge to earth creates around them a plasma sheath that eventually attains a natural frequency greater than that of their communications system. A communications blackout results until the plasma dissipates.

Another idiosyncrasy of plasmas is that they are constantly rearranging their positive and negative charges so as to maintain electrical neutrality. So successful are they in this respect that a charged particle, introduced from outside, never "sees" their internal electric fields. This trait is used to great advantage in the thermionic diode—a new kind of electron tube developed to convert heat directly to electricity. It consists of two electrodes housed in a vacuum tube and connected by an outside wire. If either electrode is heated sufficiently, it gives off electrons. In effect, this means the cooler electrode is losing electrons, via the connecting wire to the hot electrode, and acquiring a net positive charge in the bargain. The electrons freed from the hot electrode now see this charge and rush to it, completing the circuit. A flow of electric current results.

This works very well for low voltages and currents, but when scientists try to step these up, something unexpected happens. So many electrons collect in the gap between the electrodes that their combined negative charge, called *space charge*, begins to restrict and even curtail the flow of electrons. To obtain higher powers, therefore, the space charge must be neutralized. This is done by filling the gap between the electrodes with a plasma. Today, most thermionic diodes employ plasmas to produce powers up to 500 watts from such heat sources as burning coal, focused sunlight, or nuclear reactions.

Plasmas can be used in yet another way to generate electric power because their free negative and positive charges create a kind of spatial storage battery. It is literally possible to attach terminals to them and force their electrons into an outside circuit to do work.

The best means for doing so is to drive the plasma across a magnetic field. Electrodes placed at right angles to this field then act as terminals, the electrons going to one and the ions to the other. Moreover, if these electrodes are connected by an insulated copper wire that happens to run through all the homes, factories, and stores of a fair-sized town, a whole community might be powered this way. This possibility is presently being explored under the formidable title of magnetohydrodynamics—MHD, for short.

Though such a system might generate millions of watts of power, it would be of the direct current variety, which is not as manageable as alternating current. True, it could be converted to the alternating form, but why not generate it that way in the first place?

This line of reasoning led RCA engineers working in Moorestown, New Jersey, to design an experimental alternating

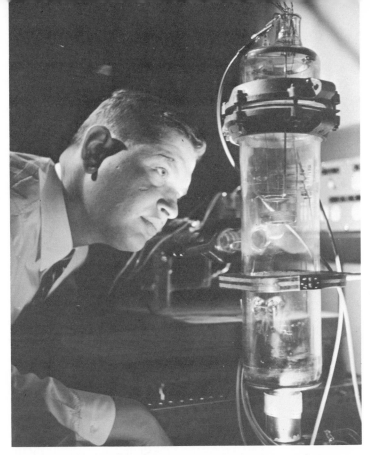

Scientists of RCA are developing a new radio-frequency technique that may be used to propel space vehicles on long interplanetary voyages. Here Dr. George A. Swartz observes experimental operation of the technique, which uses ultrahigh radio frequencies to accelerate charged particles—electrons and ions—to high velocity. With further development, this process is expected to create enough thrust for spacecraft propulsion in the gravity-free environment of outer space. In laboratory equipment shown here, particles are accelerated upward from base of glass cylinder, and their velocity is measured by probes visible in upper half of tube.

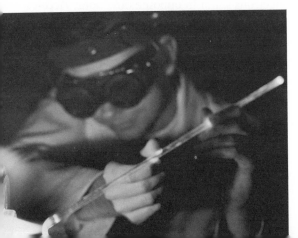

Dr. Lincoln Ekstrom melts a glass rod in the 5000°F heat of an argon plasma.

current MHD generator a few years ago. Their approach was to move an alternating electromagnetic field along a plasma chamber at a speed slower than that at which the plasma was moving inside it. This caused a string of counter-rotating loops of electric current to appear in the plasma at right angles to the field.

The upshot was that the magnetic fields inside the plasma loops gained energy and induced an electric current right back into the coils generating the controlling field. In addition to producing alternating current, this scheme provided current by induction, eliminating the need to station electrodes directly in the plasma stream where they erode rapidly.

The feasibility of this system was demonstrated, for the first time, when RCA scientists successfully measured a power flow of 10 watts from the plasma. Eventually, a full-scale version might produce as much power as Grand Coulee Dam.

Even more sensational in the field of power generation is the worldwide effort to produce electricity from controlled thermonuclear fusion. C Stellarator, Zeta, OGRA, Perhapsatron, Astron—these are some of the remarkable machines built or under construction in the United States and abroad to essay the task. All will depend for their success on creating and harnessing a hydrogen plasma resembling that of the sun.

In the largest of these, the C Stellarator, built by RCA and Allis-Chalmers at Princeton University for the Atomic Energy Commission, a hydrogen plasma is generated and trapped in a powerful magnetic field around whose lines of force the plasma ions and electrons spiral in opposite directions. Accelerated steadily by strong electrical fields imposed from outside, the plasma ions eventually gain so much energy that their positive electrical fields can no longer hold them apart. They begin to collide. As they do, a nuclear reaction takes place producing helium and releasing a torrent of heat, light, and other electromagnetic energy. All that remains is to collect this energy for

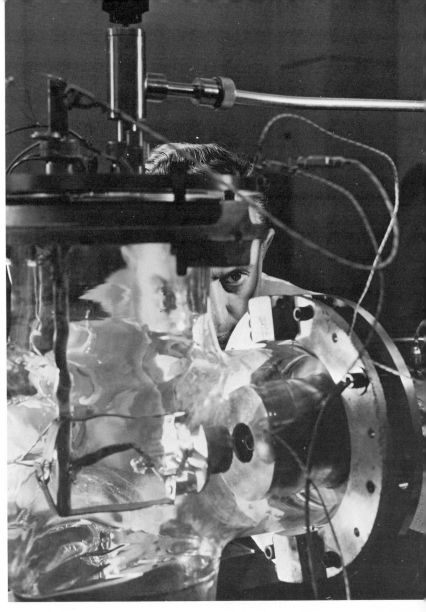

An experimental apparatus for creating charge-exchange plasma propulsion is shown undergoing test at RCA. Ions accelerated by an rf field are driven into a neutral gas in the presence of an electric field. The ion picks up an electron from the gas and continues on out the exhaust, leaving a newly created ion behind it. This new ion now undergoes the same acceleration and produces another ion of its own. The result is an avalanche of neutral particles pouring out the exhaust and providing high specific impulses for potential use in space propulsion. George Brucker is in the background.

the production of electricity either by heating water to drive a steam turbine or by some other means.

This is how it should happen in theory. In fact, however, controlled thermonuclear fusion has yet to be mastered. So far, it has proven impossible to keep the hydrogen plasma stable in the C Stellarator or in any of the other machines.

Still another facet of this magical stuff called plasma is its significant potential as a fuel for space vehicles. Thus far in our nation's space program, only chemical fuels have been used for this purpose. These provide enormous thrust for short periods, but they must be used in huge volume because they leave the rocket at relatively low speed.

Another approach is to use very little material at any given time, but to eject it at very high speed for a very long time. This is the idea behind plasma engines. Plasma engines produce too little thrust to get a rocket off the ground, but out in space, they can accelerate a vehicle to speeds upward of 100,000 miles per hour.

As part of the nation's space effort, scientists are investigating several possible methods of plasma propulsion. Of these, the most promising at present is referred to as a cyclotron-resonance system. In brief, a magnetic field is stretched along the thrust chamber with an electric field placed at right angles to it. A neutral gas is introduced, converted to a plasma by the electric field, and immediately confined by the magnetic field.

Because of the interaction of the two fields, the plasma electrons begin to spiral down the magnetic lines of force toward the exhaust nozzle. As they do, they are given periodic kicks by the electric field (in accordance with a technique known as cyclotron-resonance pumping) until they are moving at tremendous velocity.

Plasmas being what they are, these electrons no sooner issue from the exhaust than they drag the ions standing by along with them to maintain the cohesion and electrical neutrality of

their association. A plasma jet is created, and propulsion results.

Added to these plasma projects, scientists are hatching still
other plasma-dependent archetypes including gas lasers, microwave switches and amplifiers, cathodes, and acetylene-like
torches that generate temperatures above 10,000°C.

With all this research and engineering activity, both here
and abroad, it should be only a matter of time before these
playful—but powerful—electronic "blobs," called plasmas, come
to live with all of us.

Cubes of the new thermoelectric material germanium-silicon compare in size to normal playing dice. This material, developed at RCA Laboratories, will convert heat directly to electric power at temperatures up to 1000°F.

CHAPTER 14

New Sources of Electric Power

After twenty years of intensive materials research and devices development, the electronics industry is on the verge of revolutionizing the generation of electric power.

Under the cover of such ponderous and obfuscating terms as *magnetohydrodynamics, electrogasdynamics, photovoltaics, thermionics, thermoelectrics,* and *cryogenic chemistry,* electronics scientists are generating significant amounts of electric power directly from hot gases, radio waves, heat, light, and such chemical reactions as occur between super-cold liquefied gases. Both government and industry are beginning to find applications for these new energy sources.

141

In the space program, for example, all of the electricity to power the instruments and life-support equipment aboard the Apollo space capsules is provided by fuel cells. The energy is derived from electrons freed during the reaction of hydrogen with oxygen to produce water. And the electric power to run the instruments of more than 200 American space satellites—from the 5-watt Vanguard to the 400-watt Nimbus—has come from solar cells that convert sunlight directly to electricity by means of the photovoltaic effect. In addition, when the United States launched the first nuclear reactor into orbit, in 1965, all power required on board was provided by a blanket of solid-state germanium-silicon thermocouples. These devices were developed by RCA to cover the reactor and convert its heat directly to a steady 500-watt flow of electricity.

The military is also using these new power-generation techniques. For instance, the Air Force powers a hypersonic wind tunnel at the Arnold Engineering Development Center in Tullahoma, Tennessee, with a magnetohydrodynamic generator. This produces up to 20 million watts of electric power by means of a super-hot gas driven across a strong magnetic field.

In other applications, the General Electric and General Atomic companies are both building nuclear reactors that incorporate thermionic diodes to convert heat directly into electricity. The Raytheon Company of Massachusetts is testing a robot helicopter that extracts electric power by means of microwave diodes directly from a radio beam. And a New Jersey firm, Gourdine Systems, Inc., has recently developed an experimental electrogasdynamic generator, which employs a hot electrified gas moving in a narrow channel to generate up to 4 watts of electric power at 120,000 volts.

What makes all these remarkable systems different from most conventional sources of electric power is that the actual process by which they produce current involves no moving parts. This contrasts with motor-generator sets, such as are used in automobiles, and with dynamos typically used in steam generating plants and hydroelectric dams. Taken together, these items generate about 95 percent of the world's electric power, but both sources depend on the motion of a mechanical armature in a magnetic field to do so.

The reason this difference is so important is that any generator that depends on mechanical motion must inevitably suffer energy losses due to inertia, friction, and heating. As a result, the very best steam generating plants are only about 41 percent efficient. There is also a problem of life. Anything that rotates on an axle as fast as the armature in a dynamo is bound to wear out rapidly.

Although conventional batteries do not have moving parts and can be as much as 99 percent efficient in converting chemical energy to electric current, they cannot achieve the powers of a dynamo, and they have one fatal flaw. They consume their own electrodes, and thus, their life is sharply limited. Further, because batteries generally employ such materials as lead and zinc, they are very heavy, especially when linked in series to gain higher outputs. In a space application, this can be a debilitating penalty.

It was just such considerations, following World War II, that led the military services and, later, the National Aeronautics and Space Administration to seek alternatives to the dynamo and the battery. What they sought were new power sources that would be self-contained, lightweight, mobile, small size, long-lived, reliable, rugged, reasonably efficient, and not too expensive. As if that were not enough, the military made quiet operation a *sine qua non* as well!

The electronics industry and others accepted the challenge. When they started, there were only three known ways to generate significant amounts of electricity: electrostatically, electrochemically, and electrodynamically. The electrostatic principle—storing electric charges on an insulator and then bringing it into contact with a conductor—was first embodied in a machine by Baron Otto von Guericke, of Magdeburg, Germany, in 1660. It has since found its way into certain hand-cranked generators for use in emergencies.

The electrochemical principle—involving chemical reactions that release excess electrons to a conductor in the course of their progress—was discovered in 1794 by Count Alessandro Volta, in Italy, and led him to the invention of the storage battery.

Finally, the electrodynamic principle—which entails the mechanical motion of a conductor across a magnetic field—was used in a practical machine for the first time by Antonio Pacinotti, in Italy, during the early 1860s. It has since led to the dynamo.

Most of the initial research toward new power sources was directed along these three lines. For example, Gourdine Systems chose the electrostatic principle and, for the past several years, has been developing a family of experimental electrogasdynamic generators. These devices heat various gases to temperatures upward of 1500°C and then allow them to

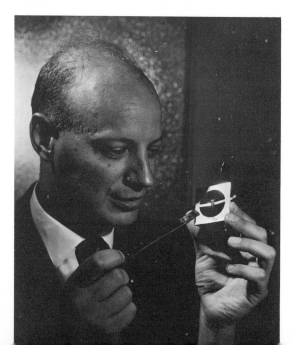

Dr. Paul Rappaport points to a self-healing solar cell at center of test fixture. It is something like a self-healing gas tank in that it incorporates a reservoir of lithium atoms which are free to move into and neutralize areas in the cell as they are damaged by cosmic radiation.

"blow" along a narrow channel through an electrical field that strips electrons from the gas atoms and sucks them into a nearby electrode. The momentum of the stripped atoms—now converted to positively charged ions—carries them beyond this field toward a negatively charged electrode. Since this second electrode is attached to the first by a wire running outside the machine, the ions really recombine with their own lost electrons, thus completing the circuit. Before recombining, however, the electrons can be made to do work as they run along the wire by hooking it into a motor, light bulb, or other electrical device.

The Avco Corporation, on the other hand, is using the electrodynamic approach. Since 1954, its engineers have been building experimental, magnetohydrodynamic generators that are suggestive of the Gourdine approach in that they heat various gases to very high temperatures (about 2000°C) and blow them along a large duct. However, the gas is so hot that nearly all its atoms are broken down into their constituent electrons and ions so that they form a gaseous plasma. When this plasma blows across a powerful magnetic field, set at right angles to its path, the electrons are forced up and the ions down toward electrodes protruding right into the stream. Since the electrodes are also linked by an outside wire, a current immediately flows with the potential to do work. In effect, the Avco machine is a dynamo whose armature has been replaced by a streaming gas plasma.

Allis-Chalmers, Esso Research, Pratt & Whitney, Westinghouse, and other chemically oriented companies not unexpectedly decided to try the electrochemical approach. They reasoned that if materials lighter than zinc and lead could be used, and if they could produce more free electrons while interacting, a new, high-power, lightweight battery might be developed. Further, if these chemicals consumed only each other and not their respective electrodes, a battery could be made that could be constantly replenished. The result is the fuel cell.

However, certain electronics companies were not satisfied with any of these traditional approaches. They felt that with the coming of the transistor and semiconductor technology, large amounts of electric power were no longer required to operate electronic devices and circuits. Furthermore, a hard look at the challenge thrown down by the military services and by the space agency revealed that both were primarily interested in generating power to operate control circuits, sensors, communications equipment, navigational devices, and computers. Since all these were being rapidly transistorized, they did not need big power sources.

Though electrostatics, electrochemistry, and electrodynamics were the accepted ways to generate electricity, they were certainly not the only ones. Vacuum tubes that converted radio waves to electricity, photocells that converted light to electricity, thermionic diodes and solid-state thermocouples that converted heat to electricity—all had been made and used by the electronics industry for decades. But they produced only feeble amounts of electricity—power measured in hundredths or thousandths of a watt or less. They obviously could not be used to power even transistor circuits unless they were greatly improved. Fortunately, the means for such improvement were at hand in the same semiconductor technology that had been used to develop the transistor.

In 1954, researchers at the Bell Telephone Laboratories demonstrated what this new technology could do by developing a flat array of 432 semiconductor devices, dubbed *solar cells*, that could produce 10 watts of electricity from direct sunlight. This array was later installed atop a telephone pole in a Georgia community to power the electronic amplifiers of a rural telephone line. Each cell in the array was a flat, single crystal of silicon incorporating impurities whose atoms produced a scarcity of electrons on its top—p side (positive)—and an excess of electrons on its bottom—n side (negative).

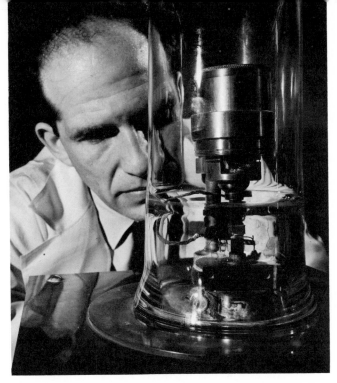

Dr. Benjamin Abeles monitors test of a germanium-
silicon thermocouple under conditions of high heat and
high vacuum. Such cells have been used to produce 500
watts of electric power directly from the heat of an
orbiting nuclear reactor.

At the atomic level, the situation thus created is comparable
to a theater whose seats (atoms) possess a positive electric
charge when not occupied by an electron. On the n side, these
"seats" are filled to overflowing and an SRO crowd of electron
"standees" mills in the aisles. On the p side, just the opposite
is made to occur, and a substantial number of empty seats is
produced.

Between these two sides, moreover, an electrically charged
"aisle," known as a *p-n junction,* is formed that prevents the
free n-side electrons from crossing over to occupy the empty
p-side seats.

If light is now shone on the p side, the relatively few electrons seated there acquire sufficient energy to leave their places
and cross the junction to join the electron crush on the n side.

The n side cannot accommodate any more electrons, however, and the new arrivals are accepted only at the expense of electrons milling near the n-side exit (a metal contact). These are shoved, willy-nilly, into a wire that runs around to the p-side entrance (another metal contact). Once in the wire these electrons see the empty p-side seats and rush to fill them, only to have the light shining there send them back across the junction to start the cycle all over again.

In short, when a solar cell is exposed to light, current flows out of its n side and into its p side through an outside conductor which can be attached to any electrical device to produce work. Moreover, it has been found that if such cells are . tied together, their cumulative currents can be substantial. In fact, in our own day, solar-cell arrays capable of producing several thousand watts are under development.

In the light of this experience, semiconductor technology was next applied to thermocouples, initially by a firm which later became part of the Minnesota Mining & Manufacturing Company. Alloys of lead telluride were "doped" with trace impurities and shaped to produce p-type and n-type legs, which were subsequently bonded to a copper crossbeam to form a U-shaped structure. Finally, a wire was attached to the ends of the legs.

Heat applied to the copper crossbeam of such a structure immediately drives the unseated electrons down to the bottom of the n leg. This causes a chain reaction of electrons moving from the copper into the n leg and of seated electrons moving forward from the p leg into the copper. Once again, this latter movement produces many empty atomic seats near the bottom of the p leg. The electrons, at the bottom of the n leg, move along the wire to fill these seats, and electric current begins to flow.

Thermoelectric arrays, built from such semiconductor thermocouples, now generate hundreds of watts of electricity using various heat sources and are expected eventually to reach the thousand-watt level.

Although thermionic diodes are not semiconductors—rather, they are vacuum tubes—they deserve mention because they too have been transformed into significant power producers by several electronics companies. They work on the same principle as all vacuum tubes—heat applied to a metal electrode inside causes electrons to pop off into the surrounding vacuum. If this electrode is linked by an outside wire to a second electrode nearby, the latter will acquire a positive charge, since it is losing electrons to the first via the wire. It then will attract the electrons in the vacuum, thus completing the circuit.

Inherently rugged and capable of enduring high temperatures, thermionic diodes are particularly well suited for use in nuclear reactors and in association with radioisotope heat sources. They have already yielded as much as 400 watts of electric power and should be able to produce 1,000 watts before long.

A spate of recent developments in the generation of electricity is tending to erase the artificial distinction traditionally made between electronics and the electric power industry. In the process, new and more versatile ways are being found to generate the *vis electrica,* as Sir William Gilbert called it, that is needed to sustain and abet the commercial growth, the industrial metabolism, and the social progress of modern civilization.

Eyebrow tweezers are used to hold a tiny but complete microwave amplifier built entirely of integrated circuits. Such units may put microwave power at the disposal of the average consumer one day.

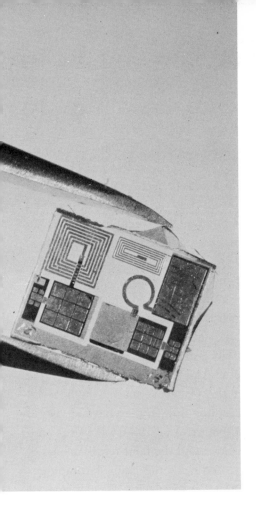

CHAPTER 15

Microwave Power Play

After years of subordination to the communications industry as a medium for carrying two-way radio messages, cross-country telephone conversations, and broadcast television programs, *microwaves*—radio waves that oscillate along wires or through space at roughly 100 million to 33 billion cycles per second—are coming into their own as a unique source of wireless power for use in home, industry, and national defense.

Of the new tasks now being assigned to them, one of the most impressive occurs in the 2-mile-long linear accelerator at Stanford University. Here a gallery of klystron tubes, producing microwaves oscillating 2,800,000,000 times per second, is

being used to "pump" electrons to energies of 20 billion electron volts and to speeds approaching 186,000 miles per second,
whereupon they are sent crashing into target atoms at the business end of the accelerator.

The atomic debris thus created is then collected and analyzed
in hopes that it will provide clues to the composition and
architecture of nuclear substance. The pumping action and
acceleration take place because the electric fields associated
with the electrons and those associated with the electromagnetic microwaves interact in such a way as to cause the electrons to surf on the waves and be whisked the length of the
machine, like so many electronic surfboard riders.

Equally impressive is the use being made of microwave
power by Cornell University astronomers working with the
1,000-foot radio telescope at Arecibo, Puerto Rico. Over the
past few years, whenever the planet Venus has approached
close to earth (within 50 million miles), they have employed
the telescope, first, to send powerful microwave pulses toward
it and, second, to receive and record the faint return echoes of
those pulses. In this way, and with the help of computers,
they have presently succeeded in producing a radar map of
one-third of the planet's surprisingly rugged surface. Eventually, they expect to map all of it with the same resolution that
would be obtainable with the world's largest optical telescopes
if it were not for the planet's impenetrable cloud cover.

Then, there is side-looking radar, a very ingenious application of microwave power whereby an airplane can make a continuous map of the terrain to either side of its flight path—a
map that looks very much like a photograph when fully processed. It is made possible by a kind of radar holography through
which the changes in wavelength produced in a radar pulse, as
a result of striking objects at various heights and distances on
the ground, are converted to an optical interference pattern on
film. When a laser beam is shone through this film and through

H. John Prager places silicon wafer containing four avalanche diodes into cavity where it will generate several hundred watts of pulsed microwave power.

a chain of lenses to a second film, a two-dimensional reconstruction of the original scene is immediately registered on the
latter.

Yet another novel application of microwaves—the transmission of electric power over short distances without wires—is
being explored by the Raytheon Company. What has been
achieved so far is a small helicopter equipped with a 6-foot
rotor and arrays of solid-state diodes that convert microwave
energy to electric current. This current is subsequently used
to power the rotor and lift the helicopter some 50 feet into the
air where it hovers, so long as microwaves are directed at it
from a radar dish below. Such a pilotless helicopter might one
day be used as a TV relay, a military observation platform, or
a means for directing air or ground traffic.

Finally, there is the resurgent field of microwave cooking
and drying. Recently, RCA announced that it has developed a
microwave tube that makes it possible to roast a 16-pound
turkey in seventy minutes, bake a cake in four, or fry strips
of bacon in less than fifty seconds. In a similar vein, the
Coventry Evening Telegraph and the London Evening
Standard, both British newspapers, are currently using microwaves to dry four-color newsprint at rates of 1,000 feet per
minute. Both of these uses are made possible by virtue of the
fact that water molecules do not have uniform electric charges.
They are slightly negative on one end and slightly positive on
the other so that, when irradiated by microwaves, they begin
to rotate at very high speed with the result that the material of
which they are part undergoes instant, internal heating
through friction.

Though the very first radio waves deliberately produced by
man were microwaves—short bursts oscillating at 100 million
cycles per second generated by the German physicist Heinrich
Hertz in 1887—they had little power and did no more than
confirm the existence of radio waves as predicted by James
Clerk Maxwell some twenty years earlier.

It was a beginning, however. Hertz had used an electric spark jumping periodically between two metal terminals, in the manner of a modern spark plug, to generate his micro-waves. (This explains, incidentally, why the starting of a nearby car often creates static in a TV picture. The spark plugs are broadcasting!) As a result, the next quarter-century of radio development was dominated by the use of spark gaps as the primary source of radio waves, though at much lower radio frequencies, and radio operators the world over acquired the nickname of "Sparks," in amused recognition of the way they produced their long-distance dots and dashes.

Sparking has since been abandoned as a means for generating man-made radio pulses, though very recently, it was cited, in its natural form, as being responsible for the existence of "whistlers"—low-frequency radio waves that travel along the lines of force of the earth's magnetic field and are now known to be generated by lightning, the biggest spark of them all.

The groundwork for getting away from the spark gap and its rather impotent oscillations was laid in 1907 when Lee De Forest invented the *audion*. In essence, it was a glass bulb housing, in partial vacuum, a source of electrons (*cathode*), a faucet for controlling their flow (*grid*), and a drain (*anode*) for piping them back to the cathode through an outside circuit.

De Forest found that when he hooked this device into a dc electrical circuit so that its cathode gained a strong negative charge, its grid a weaker negative charge, and its anode a posi-tive one, it could be used to amplify selected radio signals by running leads from its grid to an antenna that resonated in sympathy with those signals. What was happening was that the charge (voltage) on the grid was varying from more to less negative, in perfect step with the positive-to-negative oscilla-tions occurring in the incoming radio signal. This, in turn, had the effect of raising and lowering the volume of current flow-ing through the grid to the anode. Thus, De Forest had devised a mechanism for impressing the weak, oscillatory likeness of a train of radio waves propagating through space onto a relatively powerful electric current flowing in a circuit. Such is the basis for radio wave amplification even today.

Since it was an amplifier, the audion as such did not replace the spark gap as a source of radio waves. But, it did give ideas to several radio engineers and, in 1914, led Alexander Meissner, in Germany, to build a similar tube into a circuit that sent part of its output back to its cathode and grid. This had the effect of making the tube oscillate, or "ring," just as water pipes oscillate when there is pressure feedback between faucet and main water valve. In the case of Meissner's circuit, however, the vibrations were not mechanical, but electromagnetic, and the first vacuum-tube oscillator for generating radio waves was born.

By the mid-1920s triodes of this kind had been perfected to the point where they were producing radio waves in the millions-of-cycles-per-second range with powers up to 20,000 watts. Not only did these usher in the era of voice broadcasting, but they prepared the way for such men as Sir Robert Watson

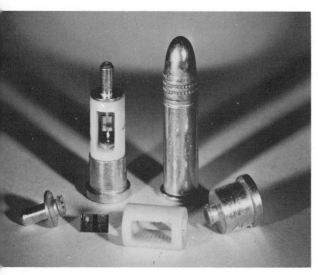

A new, solid-state source of microwave power is shown encased and in disassembled form in comparison with a standard .22 caliber bullet. This unit consists of four avalanche diodes in series and produces pulses of microwave power measured in the several hundred watt range.

Watt, in England, Dr. Robert Page, of the U.S. Naval Research Laboratory in Washington, Drs. Irving Wolff and Ernest Linder, of RCA, and several others to realize the next major outgrowth of radio research—*radar*.

Guglielmo Marconi himself, as early as 1922, had proposed that radio transmitters be installed on shipboard to detect the presence and range of other ships in the vicinity, especially at night or in a fog. Indeed, the fact that radio waves are reflected by metal objects, or other electrical conductors in their path, had been known since the turn of the century and, in 1925, had led the British physicists Edward Appleton and Myles Barnett to establish the existence and measure the height of the ionosphere by bouncing a radio signal off it. The concept of such an electrically conducting layer in the earth's upper atmosphere had been postulated by Arthur Kennelly, of Harvard University, and Oliver Heaviside, in England, in 1902, to explain how radio waves propagate around the world. Its existence was by no means certain, however, until Appleton and Barnett performed their critical radar experiment.

Despite this work and suggestions such as Marconi's, radar was slow in coming, largely because the radio frequencies man could generate were too low and their power too meager. Low frequencies meant long wavelengths—hundreds of feet from crest to crest in the propagating waves. This was just too long for them to reflect from anything smaller than the broadside of an ocean liner, insofar as meaningful detection was concerned.

What was needed were higher frequencies, shorter wavelengths, and much more power. By 1935, all three were being achieved by the triode. It was oscillating at well above 100 million cycles per second, in some cases, radiating thousands of watts of power and producing radio waves that were only a few feet from crest to crest. This meant that it could be used to detect airplanes—and just in time, too, for Nazi Germany was building an awesome air force and preparing to launch what finally became World War II. Thus, it was the effort to achieve long-distance, high-resolution radar that first gave man the ability to generate significant amounts of microwave power, and it was perfection of the high-frequency triode, just prior to World War II, that made it possible.

Although the triode proved to be more than a match for the German air force when the time came, it was not so successful in meeting the challenge of the German submarines that began to prowl the shipping lanes of the North Atlantic in the early 1940s. The wavelengths of the radio waves it generated, though measured in feet only, were still too long. What was needed was an oscillator that would produce radio waves only a few inches from crest to crest—short enough to be reflected from the slender periscopes of these submarines when they were poked above the ocean surface.

To meet this requirement, radio engineers turned to the magnetron—a different kind of vacuum tube invented by Albert Hull at the General Electric Company, in 1921, and brought to a state of practicality for high frequencies, in 1927, by Jinjiro Okabe in Japan. The magnetron produced radio waves that were only inches from crest to crest by "boiling" electrons from a central cathode surrounded by a cylindrical anode which had been split so that each half of it was alternately negative and then positive. By means of a magnetic field stretched along the length of the tube, these electrons could be forced to go consistently to that half of the anode that was negative, causing the tube to oscillate in the billions-of-cycles-per-second range with hundreds, and eventually, thousands of watts of radiated power.

Then, in 1939, using the theory of *velocity modulation* first propounded by Frederick Llewellyn at Bell Laboratories some six years before, Russell and Sigurd Varian, two talented brothers working at Stanford University on the problem of

Looking skyward. This radar antenna at Patrick Air Force Base, Florida, scans the skies as part of the United States' global satellite tracking network. It is capable of pinpointing an object 32,000 miles away within a few yards of its true position.

generating microwave power at high frequency, invented the *klystron* tube.

The klystron differed from the triode in that the mobs of electrons streaming from its cathode did not rush helter-skelter through a grid toward an anode. Instead, they passed through a circular metal cavity shaped like an automobile tire. When an alternating electric current was applied to this cavity, it tended to shape the electron stream into a salami string of electron bunches by regularly slowing down the fast electrons and speeding up the slow ones. The stream then passed through a second cavity where the uneven electric fields associated with these bunches induced uneven, or fluctuating, "image" currents on the inner surface of the cavity. Part of these were then fed back to the first cavity causing the whole tube to "ring" at very high frequencies, like an electromagnetic tuning fork. The rest were sent to a microwave antenna, which behaved, as always, like a great electromagnetic sounding board for transmission purposes.

Although the triode, the magnetron, and the klystron are now being challenged by such solid-state microwave sources as "overlay" transistors, avalanche diodes, and Gunn effect oscillators used in either their pure or so-called limited space charge accumulation (LSA) mode, none has so far been able to match the vacuum tube as a source of power. The tiny semiconductor chips of which they are made simply have not been able to take the punishing voltages, electric currents, and heat associated with the generation of super powers.

However, this situation may be about to change. Cornell University scientists W. Keith Kennedy, Jr., and Lester Eastman recently reported driving a Gunn effect device to oscillate at 7,700,000,000 cycles per second, producing pulses with a whopping power of 615 watts! Similarly, H. John Prager and Sherman Weisbrod, working under the direction of Dr. Kern Chang at RCA Laboratories, recently discovered a new effect in certain avalanche diodes that has made it possible for them to generate 1-billion-cycle-per-second pulses with a power of 1,000 watts!

These are incredible powers to emanate from solid-state devices, so tiny they would fit comfortably under a fingernail, and, when juxtaposed with recent advances made in building integrated circuits for microwave equipment, give promise that up to 1 million watts of pulsed microwave power may one day be available from a few poker-chip-sized wafers of semiconductor material. Indeed, a step in that direction is already being taken by such firms as Texas Instruments, Inc., Emerson Electric Company, and RCA, which are attempting, independently, to build *phased array* radars, a new type that uses solid-state circuits to scan the sky electronically rather than mechanically.

In summary, advances in electron-tube technology, applied to the generation and control of electromagnetic energy at microwave frequencies, have given birth to a novel source of power so versatile it can be used to probe the atom, map the planets, dry newsprint, cook meals, or transmit electricity without the aid of wires. Moreover, new solid-state technology, now on the horizon, promises to extend this versatility still further in the years ahead.

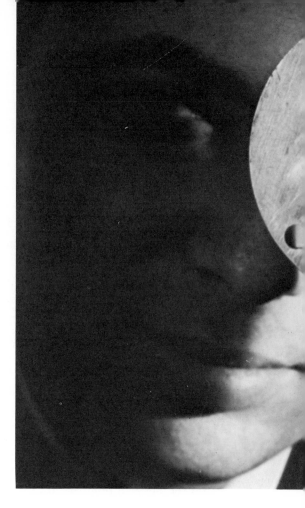

Dr. Albert Clorfeine looks down a section of waveguide toward the first superconductive microwave amplifier ever developed.

CHAPTER 16

Beyond
Microwave

After twenty years of trench warfare along the microwave frontiers of the electromagnetic spectrum communications scientists have opened a full-scale offensive on the technological Maginot Line standing between them and the use of frequencies above microwave—those including millimeter, submillimeter, infrared, and light waves. Advancing behind a screen of heavy armor bristling with such high-frequency assault gear as klystrons, magnetrons, avalanche diodes, and parametric amplifiers, these research forces have already pushed to the outskirts of the millimeter frequencies and, through the laser, have even breached the bastions of infrared and visible light.

163

At stake in this contest is the future of a communications industry whose channels soon stand to be swamped by a rising flood of information spilling into the air from a multiplying host of transmitting antennas inside and outside the earth's atmosphere.

The day is already in sight, in fact, when such transmission forms as am and fm radio, short wave, international telephone and teleprinting, television, and radar will not admit of simultaneous operation without producing a composite din of electromagnetic cross talk, intermodulation, and fade-out that will be impossible to decipher.

To postpone this day and the stringent program of frequency rationing that it would elicit from national governments around the world, communications researchers are spending their energies devising arch techniques and artful circuitry that will allow them to pack information into every nook and cranny of

Dr. Arie Eichenbaum with a plasma cathode which he developed for use in millimeter wave experiments.

today's transmission channels. Representative of these efforts are multiplexing and pulse code modulation (PCM).

In multiplexing, many hundreds of different messages are combined for transmission on a single "carrier" frequency by a technique resembling that used when a group of notes on a piano is combined and struck together as a single chord. The only difference occurs at the receiver where, in the case of radio, this "chord" is picked up and broken down into its individual "notes" again so as to make possible retrieval of the separate information contained in each. The effect of multiplexing, therefore, is to increase dramatically the amount of information that can be carried simultaneously by a single radio channel.

In the case of pulse code modulation, on the other hand, all information is transformed into a digital code—like Morse code—and transmitted as a pattern of ons and offs, which can be recognized and reconstructed into a meaningful voice message or TV picture by a decoder at the receiver. The effect is to reduce the number of individual pulses needed to send a single message on the carrier wave and, therefore, to increase the total number of messages that can be carried.

So much for the ingenious legerdemain being developed to ward off the day when communications transmitters may well turn into monumental electromagnetic "towers of babble." These techniques, though interesting and valuable, do not strike at the source of the problem—the narrowness of the frequency band presently available for wireless communications.

From the time when Heinrich Hertz first confirmed the existence of radio waves, in 1887, to the conclusion of World War II, the number of frequencies that could be used for broadcasting grew steadily. By 1945, information could be manipulated over a swath of frequencies stretching from about 10,000 cycles per second (10 kHz) at the low end to 30 billion cycles per second (30 GHz) at the high end. By that time, however, the technology was played out. It was and still is largely unable to crack the next level of frequencies above microwave. Thus, while the amount of traffic carried by radio communications has mushroomed, the number of channels that can be commandeered to transport it has remained virtually unchanged since World War II.

The reasons are not hard to fathom, once it is understood that communications by electromagnetic wave are essentially the same as communications by sound wave. First, there is a need for something that will generate a tone (vocal chords in the case of speech, electronic oscillators in the case of radio) and second, for something that will modulate, or vary, that tone in a periodic way (tongue and lips in the case of voice, electron tubes or transistors in the case of radio).

One other item. Because the electromagnetic tones generated by radio oscillators may be too weak to be detected by the time they reach their intended receivers, many amplifiers are employed all along the line to strengthen and sustain them. Until recently, there has been no direct equivalent to these in sound.

It is the almost total absence of simple oscillators and amplifiers operative at electromagnetic frequencies beyond microwave that, so far, has stymied electronics scientists and engineers in their quest for new communications channels in the millimeter and submillimeter portions of the spectrum. At many laboratories around the nation this quest has led to such novel developments as (1) the avalanche transit time diode, a semiconductive device made to undergo controlled electrical breakdown at just the point where it begins to oscillate and to produce radio waves in the millimeter domain; (2) the Gunn effect oscillator, whose compound semiconductor structure, developed by John Gunn at IBM in 1963, generates microwaves by forcing electric currents to move through it in bunches instead of continuously; and (3) the superconductive ampli-

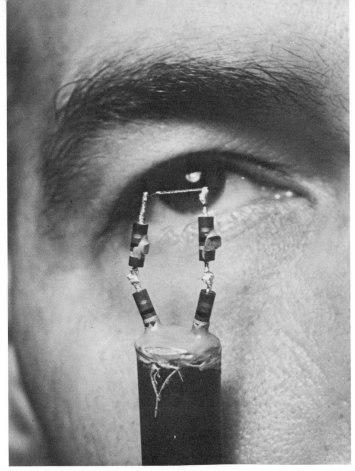

Scientist with indium antimonide filament straddling his eye. Indium antimonide will support a hole-electron plasma when proper voltages are applied.

fier, a device that amplifies microwaves when immersed in liquid helium and may one day do the same for submillimeter waves.

Equally significant is the work going forward on solid-state plasmas. Since plasmas are energetic concentrations of positively charged ions (atoms missing one or more electrons) and negatively charged electrons held together, at long range, by a mutual electrical attraction, they can exist in space or solids.

In space, plasmas generally have the appearance of luminous gases, like those seen in operating neon signs, fluorescent lights, and mercury vapor lamps. In solids, they are the product of the way electrons, freed—by application of an electric field—from the atoms composing the solid, interact with their former hosts as they career through the material. Strangely enough, this interaction has all the earmarks of a gaseous plasma phenomenon and has been used by scientists to generate high-frequency millimeter waves.

Despite this and other substantial progress in laboratories around the world, the inability to fashion good oscillators and amplifiers continues to hamstring development of practical millimeter and submillimeter communications systems. One of the best that has been demonstrated so far has been built for the U.S. Navy by Sylvania Electric Products, Inc. Delivered early in 1968, the system makes it possible to conduct two-way voice communications in the 36 billion to 38 billion cycle-per-second range over line-of-sight distances of up to 15 miles. This distance is cut to about 5 miles in heavy rain or fog, however, due to atmospheric absorption.

The extreme difficulty experienced in getting from microwave to millimeter wave frequencies, on the electromagnetic scale, has not been repeated in going from microwaves to microns (light wavelengths), however. The development of the laser has made the latter surprisingly easy.

Now available in a variety of forms, the laser is the first device capable of generating and amplifying light in the electromagnetic enclave containing infrared, visible, and ultraviolet frequencies. Moreover, because its output is coherent and nearly monochromatic, the laser can be modulated or varied in accordance with the same techniques developed for the lower radio frequencies. Rudimentary am and fm light beams have already been demonstrated by several laboratories and have been made to carry conversation, music, television pictures, and radarlike pulses for use in precision range finding.

It also turns out that laser beams are an important means for generating millimeter and submillimeter waves. This is done by simply "beating" or mixing two laser beams of differing frequencies together in such a way that one subtracts from the other, creating a new frequency in the lower millimeter register.

Though the situation is still somewhat fluid, it appears that the communications industry is preparing to seize higher electromagnetic ground in its struggle to contain the information explosion.

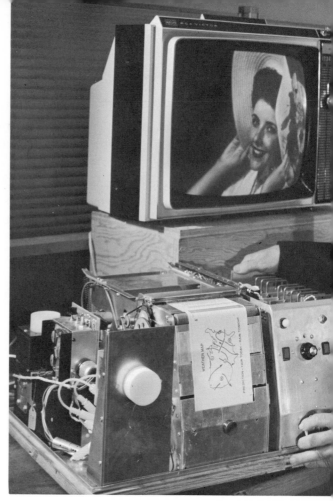

Dr. Harry F. Olson demonstrates experimental Homefax machine which makes it possible to send graphic and TV information simultaneously to the home. The work could lead to a newspaper of the air.

CHAPTER 17

Electronic
Photography

By a kind of modern alchemy that would have impressed such celebrated disciples of that medieval métier as Paracelsus or Dr. Faustus, the electronics industry has succeeded in brewing in the kilns and alembics of its research laboratories a dry, invisible, photoelectronic "ink" that may yet banish chemistry from the photographic arts.

Some measure of its power may be gained by realizing that it is the substance in which the histories of two billion-dollar industries—television and office copying—are written and with which the outlines of several future industries are now being sketched. In addition, it is the basic ingredient of facsimile transmission systems, such as those used to send news photo-

171

graphs overseas, of the Eidophor system for projecting TV pictures in theaters, and of several experimental machines presently under development in the printing, labeling, graphic arts, movie, and aerospace industries.

Clearly, this is no ordinary ink! In fact, it is an attar of electrostatic particles, an impalpable web of electrons, ions, or other charged entities that can be brushed onto an electronically insulating surface, such as glass or paper, by an electron beam or deposited as a dust of atmospheric ions created by an electric wand known as a corona discharge device.

When light, or a stream of oppositely charged particles, falls upon such a sensitized surface through a stencil, photographic transparency, or mask, it will leave an impression of the latter in the charge, just as a footstep leaves its impression in snow. The reason is that the light, or particle stream, partially or completely neutralizes the areas it strikes, producing an electrostatic "chiaroscuro" of weak and strong regions of charge that are the electrical equivalent of the dark and bright areas in the incident light.

Such an impression, or image, would not ordinarily be visible since electric charge cannot be seen. However, the industry has found that a transient reading of the image can be made by an electron beam—as in a TV camera—or a permanent image developed by dusting with so-called *triboelectric* powders, materials that acquire electric charge when rubbed against each other.

Now, it has even been shown that full-color prints can be achieved this way using light filters and different-colored triboelectric powders suspended in kerosene or some other insulating liquid. Each primary color is laid down separately, one atop the other, whereupon they all blend to form a full-color image which is permanently fixed by heating.

Such a process may one day make it possible to build vending machines that produce color prints while you wait, machines that provide limited runs of color promotional materials and merchandising items for which it would be uneconomic to make printing plates, and machines for use in color proofing or for printing full-sized billboard illustrations. It might even make possible facsimile broadcasting of color copy and photographs directly to the home.

The first realization that electrostatic charges could produce visual effects of a graphic nature goes back to 1777 when a German physicist by the name of Georg Lichtenberg noticed that dust particles on a cake of resin to which he had previously applied an electric spark had arranged themselves in a sunburst pattern of striking beauty. Such patterns were immediately dubbed *Lichtenberg figures* and formed a subject of intensive study for many years thereafter.

In 1788, an equally obscure investigator by the name of Dominique Villarsy, a Frenchman, discovered that a triboelectric powder mix of minium (red lead) and sulfur, sprinkled on the Lichtenberg figures through a muslin bag, could detect whether the electrostatic charges responsible for them had a positive or negative sign. This introduced the idea of using triboelectric powders to develop electrostatic images.

A slightly oblique step in this progression was made around 1842 by Sir Francis Ronalds, in England, when he succeeded in building a machine he called an *electrograph* for use in detecting changes in atmospheric electricity. This machine was the first electrostatic recorder and has since led, indirectly, to such things as the modern videograph printer—a high-speed device that prints copy electrostatically.

Yet another and novel contribution was made by Sir Joseph Swan, also in England, in 1897, when he found that a soft layer of resin would shrivel or become deformed under the influence of electrostatic charges lying on its surface. He further observed that the deformations, in the form of tiny corrugations or wrinkles, were really Lichtenberg figures which could be developed by dusting and fixed by the simple expedient of hardening the resin. Amazing as this effect was, it was promptly forgotten until A. Morris Thomas in England rediscovered it in 1945. Today, it is the basis of a new electrostatic recording technique known as *thermoplastic recording*.

Of course, none of these early efforts produced pictures, and all seemed to be mere oddities in the new science of electricity. Then, in 1923, Dr. Vladimir K. Zworykin, working in the research laboratories of the Westinghouse Electric Corporation, in Pittsburgh, produced the first successful all-electronic vacuum tube for use as the eye of a television camera. The key to its operation was a thin aluminum plate oxidized on one side. When light from the scene to be televised fell on the oxide, it created an electrostatic image that remained on the oxide long enough for an electron beam, originating at the other end of the tube, to scan back and forth across it and be converted by it to a pulsating television signal suitable for broadcast.

This all-electronic vacuum tube was the forerunner of the famous *iconoscope*, the first practical TV camera tube, and it established the vital role that could be played by electrostatics not only in television but in electronics generally.

A few years later, an ingenious Hungarian physicist by the name of Paul Selenyi, working at the Tungsram Research Laboratories in Budapest, carried the early electrographic putterings of Sir Ronalds a giant step forward with the development of a technique for making the images generated on the inside face of a cathode-ray tube (similar to a TV picture tube) visible on the outside by dusting the face with a positively charged powder.

He moved on from there to a cathode-ray tube whose thick glass face he replaced with a thin celluloid window. Against this, he pressed a sheet of insulating material behind which was a positive electrode. As the electron beam carrying picture information played across the celluloid, it poked through and deposited a varying electrostatic charge, or image, on the insulating sheet. Later, this image was developed by sprinkling it with a positively charged powder.

Finally, Selenyi got rid of the vacuum altogether, built the components of the cathode-ray tube in air, and let the electron beam create negative ions—in this case, oxygen atoms with more than their normal complement of electrons—which were drawn to a drum covered with a sheet of coated paper. The resulting charge image was then developed as usual. He actually produced recognizable photographic images this way in the mid-1930s.

Interestingly enough, the ideas of Selenyi have been carried forward, in various guises, and today are best represented in the *videograph printer*, a machine manufactured by the A. B. Dick Company which produces copy on 8½-inch-wide paper at the rate of 180 feet per second. The heart of the unit is a *pin tube*, a cathode-ray type with a mesh of tungsten pins embedded end-on in its face. When the tube's electron beam scans across these pins, it charges them according to a selected type

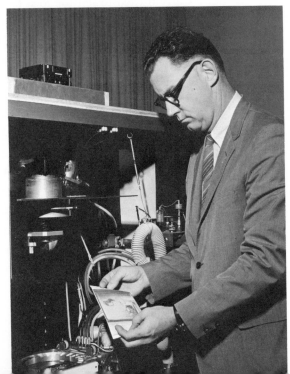

Dr. D. A. Ross examines a color print produced by a new color Electrofax machine being worked on at RCA Laboratories.

pattern. The pins, in turn, ionize oxygen atoms nearby, which are attracted to a sheet of paper moving past at high speed, whereupon the pattern laid down by the ions is developed and fixed. Such units are especially useful as print-out machines for computers.

Thus, by 1935, electrostatics was firmly entrenched in the camera tubes of the budding television industry, producing transient images for reading by an electron beam. And the industry was struggling to find the right combinations of charges and powders (toners) to produce permanent photographic images.

Then, in 1938, Chester Carlson, an unknown patent attorney working in Astoria, Long Island, with a German refugee physicist by the name of Otto Kornei, succeeded in producing on a sulfur-coated plate an electrostatic image of a date which Carlson had written on a glass slide. They dusted the plate to develop the image and pressed it against a sheet of waxed paper which they then heated to soften the wax and allowed to cool. The result was a perfect image of the date fixed on the paper. Thus was xerography born.

Carlson tried to sell the idea to several companies as a way of producing copies of important documents but met with no success until the Battelle Memorial Institute in Columbus, Ohio, took an interest in 1944.

Battelle added a new twist in the years that followed. Rather than use sulfur to hold the electrostatic charge, it hit upon the idea of using amorphous or noncrystalline selenium, a particularly good *photoconductor* and an insulating material that becomes conducting when exposed to light.

At about this time, 1948, the Haloid Company in upstate New York, having conceived a more than casual interest in the work, sought and received a license from Battelle to develop the system commercially. Following that, Haloid changed its name to the Xerox Corporation and, in 1950, produced the first in a successful series of electrostatic copying machines.

Close-up of weather map sent through experimental Homefax equipment.

At about this time, too, Harold G. Greig, working at RCA Laboratories, began investigating the possibility of using the photoconductor zinc oxide to achieve a similar end. His idea was to incorporate the zinc oxide in a paper on which electrostatic images could be made directly without the intervention of a master.

His efforts were eventually crowned with success, and in 1954, Greig announced the development of the new process which RCA began to license under the name *Electrofax*. A number of standard office copiers currently employ this process, and several manufacturers currently produce the special paper upon which it is based.

Interesting as these developments were, they were exceeded in bravura (if not in economic potential) by an entirely unique application of electrostatics then coming into prominence, though originally conceived as early as 1939. This was

Eidophor—a spectacular system being developed by Dr. Fritz Fischer at the Swiss Polytechnic Institute in Zurich for use in projecting television pictures onto a theater screen.

The idea was to use the surface-deformation capabilities of electrostatic charges first observed by Swan. Instead of producing permanent images as the latter had done, however, Fischer proposed to build a system which would produce transient deformation images that would last just long enough to be projected onto a screen. In pursuit of this goal, he and, after his death in 1947, his successors built a complex TV picture tube whose electron beam drew charge images in the form of momentary ripples on a thin film of oil inside the tube. At the same time an intense light shone through the oil, was diffracted by the ripples, and emerged into a special optical system which projected flawless pictures to a size of some 30 by 40 feet. The system was an instant success, proved equally adept at producing black-and-white or color, and is presently installed in several theaters both here and abroad.

In 1959, still another variation of photography by electrostatic deformation—this one yielding permanent images—was developed by William Glenn of the General Electric Company. What he did was to replace the oil film of the Eidophor system with a thermoplastic material which could be developed by heating and rapid cooling, in the traditional way.

A novel achievement in this general area, too, is the *dielectric tape camera* developed by RCA. This unit, for the first time, combines elements of both optical and electronic photography. It can be used to take pictures optically—the incoming light produces an electrostatic image on a special insulating film— and then used to read them out electronically like the target of a TV camera tube. It has been proposed for use in taking closeup pictures of the planets because of its speed and its ability to erase and reuse its own film.

Although all these systems are impressive, each in its own

way, they are limited in their applications by the fact that they require a vacuum and an electron beam. More versatile systems which obviate this irksome detail have now been proposed variously by RCA, Xerox, and General Electric. One, formally referred to as *frost imaging* and informally as "cracklefax," produces, on specially prepared materials, images which appear white against a clear background and which can be projected by either the reflection or transmission of light.

Another, variations of which have been devised by RCA and General Electric, involves the use of a transparent photoconductive material dissolved in a plastic film. When charged, exposed to an image, heated and allowed to cool, the film continues to appear transparent though it now contains a deformation image in the form of tiny ripples frozen on its surface. A special *schlieren* optical system is all that is required to read it out.

So far, electronic photography is not so fast nor so sensitive as optical photography, in most applications. But, it is getting there as witness television, facsimile, the office copier, and electrostatic printing. With such a list of accomplishments already on the record, can the electrostatic "Brownie" be very far behind?

A pulsed ruby laser sends a short burst of coherent light smashing through a sapphire crystal.

CHAPTER 18

The
Coming Age
of Light

Man is a creature of light—biologically, socially, theologically, and aesthetically . . .

. . . biologically, because he is the latest link in an evolutionary chain that began to be forged some three billion years ago in the foundries of photosynthesis—that miraculous process by which sunlight interacts with certain molecules to nourish (and perhaps once to initiate) plant life.

. . . socially, because he has the diurnal rhythm of the sun built into his bones. Work, feeding, recreation, study, conversation, war—virtually all human activities are conducted in the light of day or in the narrow effulgence of candle, wick, or heated filament.

. . . theologically, because his eye has prejudiced him against the dark. As constant as the speed of light itself is the notion that Providence is Light and evil is the Prince of Darkness. In consequence, the sun, moon, stars, lightning, fire—indeed, all the natural sources of light from incandescence to phosphorescence—have been worshiped by man at one time or another if not as divinities at least as divine.

. . . aesthetically, because beauty is color and line and contrast, purity and rhythm and intensity—all qualities attributable to the effect of light playing upon form or substance.

As much out of awe as ignorance, therefore, man has been slow to perceive the nature of light and even slower to grasp the means by which to discipline its energies and harness its power directly to the engines of progress. Instead, he has been content, until very recently, to salvage for use only its grossest properties.

So vast are light's natural resources, however, so various and unique, that even these gross few have been sufficient to raise such ancient and flourishing industries as the manufacture of mirrors (which use reflection), the mining of precious gems (whose interplay of colors stems from refraction), the production of glass dishware and windows (which provide transmission), the grinding of lenses (which both focus and transmit), and the making of lamps (which provide illumination).

This state of affairs is about to change, however. After nearly a century of plumbing the mysteries of the electron and exploiting its ability to produce and control the invisible radio wave, electronics scientists and engineers are preparing to tap it anew, this time to generate and control the visible electromagnetic waves we sense as light.

Among the new tools and instruments being contemplated are point-to-point light beams that carry hundreds of thousands of radio, television, and telephone messages simultaneously; optical computers that store and process information in the forms of and at the speed of light; novel television systems that project into our homes color images that give a true sense of three dimensions to the unaided eye; long-playing phonograph records that provide high-fidelity sound and three-dimensional color pictures at the same time; microscopes without lenses that may reveal what the atom looks like for the first time; portable tools, cooking equipment, and toys that are powered directly by sunlight; heavy-duty equipment for machining, welding, and drilling refractory material with coherent light beams of high precision and prodigious power. The list is virtually without limit.

That these possibilities not only exist today but are being hotly pursued in the nation's electronics research laboratories derives from the discovery that light does more than merely illuminate the material world. It can interact with and alter it as well.

Recognition of this fact was first recorded in 1603 when a certain Italian shoemaker and would-be alchemist, né Vincenzo Cascariolo, betook himself one day to a mountain outside Bologna in search, possibly, of the fabled philosopher's stone, by whose agency, according to informed sources, any base material could be transmuted to gold.

Sometime later when the good signore descended from the mount, he carried with him a strange and marvelous stone which glowed weakly in the dark after first being exposed to sunlight. Such was the earliest recorded observation of inorganic *phosphorescence*, a discovery which has since led by many a tortuous route to the fluorescent lights of the electric industry and the television screens of its sister industry—electronics.

In 1839, 236 years later, Edmond Becquerel, a French physicist engaged in experiments with the new force called electricity, shone light on the negative terminal of a simple voltaic battery. Much to his surprise, his measuring apparatus showed that the light was causing a weak electric current to flow in the battery. What he had observed was the *photovoltaic effect,* the principle on which today's solar cell is based and by which nearly all our space satellites are powered.

Another score of years passed and then, in 1859, Julius Plücker, a German scientist studying the behavior of cathode rays in gas discharge tubes, found that the ends of these tubes often flared with a green fluorescence where these rays impacted. Herr Plücker had stumbled upon the phenomenon of *cathodoluminescence*—the effect by which the oscilloscope, the radar screen, and the television picture tube trace out their brief electronic lithographs.

This apparent connection between electricity and light was further elucidated when, in 1864, the Scottish physicist James Clerk Maxwell first conceived the theory that the nature of light is electromagnetic. Following publication of this epochal theory, a veritable avalanche of new information concerning the effect of light on matter swept down upon the scientific community.

In England, in 1873, Willoughby Smith reported finding that selenium—ordinarily a poor conductor of electricity—could be made to carry current with ease when it was exposed to light. This phenomenon, termed *photoconductivity,* has since been exploited to produce the vidicon TV camera tube, invented by Dr. Paul Weimer at RCA, and used with spectacular results in the Tiros weather satellites, the Ranger moon probes, and the Mariner interplanetary space vehicles.

In 1875, John Kerr, working in England, sought to influence light passing through a transparent crystal by applying an electric field to the crystal. This was a trick attempted by Michael Faraday in 1845 without success (though, as a consolation, Faraday did find that a *magnetic* field can exert such influence). With more sensitive instruments available to him, Kerr proceeded to demonstrate that Faraday's original hunch was right—an electric field applied to a crystal can influence a beam of light passing through it by changing its orientation. Each effect now bears the name of its discoverer, but it is Kerr's which has come to command the greater scientific attention and from which the exciting new field of electrooptics has descended.

In Germany, in 1887, still another interaction of light with solid matter was triumphantly noted by Heinrich Hertz. In experiments employing electric spark gaps (like those in a spark plug), Hertz noticed the sparks got fatter when light shone on the negative terminal of his device. He correctly surmised that the light was freeing negative charges from the terminal, in addition to those being freed by the electric field across the gap. Thus was *photoemission* discovered, and the foundations laid for the conversion-tube industry—the source of pickup tubes for TV cameras, infrared imaging tubes for seeing in the dark, and photomultipliers and image intensifiers for achieving bright views of such dim objects as distant galaxies.

Brilliant as these discoveries were, however, they were effects without an explanation. The mechanism by which light produced them continued to elude scientists, even while Joseph J. Thomson, in England, was postulating the existence of the electron (1897) and Max Planck, in Germany, was hypothesizing, in 1900, that maybe atoms absorb or emit light only in certain fixed quantities—*quanta* as he called them. This was comparable to saying that maybe milk bottles come only in quart sizes.

In 1905, Albert Einstein turned this idea on its head and finally solved the photoelectric effect by suggesting and then proving that it was not so much the atoms but the light that came in fixed, indivisible quantities (since named photons). In effect, he said it was not the bottles that came in quarts but the milk itself.

All that remained, it seemed, was to adduce a physical mechanism by which this interaction of light and solid matter could be accomplished. In 1913, Niels Bohr did just that with his famous conception of the atom as a miniature solar system, having a nucleus at its center and electrons in various orbits around it.

The next important chapter in this epic of light opened in 1923 when a Russian physicist by the name of Oleg Lossyev observed that a crystal of silicon carbide (a relative of diamond) glowed when subjected to an electric field. This was something new and bore no relation to the cathodoluminescence of Plücker since it was an electric field and not a stream of cathode rays (electrons) that produced the glow. Lossyev's was the first observation of *electroluminescence*, the process which, in 1963, produced the injection laser—a device which may make the optical computer possible.

In the laser, first reported by Theodore Maiman in 1960, the electronics industry has taken its latest and, in some ways, most impressive step toward mastering the miracle of light. To appreciate why, a brief review of the essential character of light may prove useful.

Consisting of interwoven electric and magnetic fields which vibrate at right angles to each other at a rate (for the visible spectrum) from 430 trillion to 750 trillion times per second, light propagates through space, usually as a jumble of frequencies speeding along at 186,300 miles per second. In this condition, it has amplitude (intensity), frequency (color), and direction. Also, it can have polarization.

Furthermore, if the ray of light can be so filtered or so generated that its intertwined magnetic and electric oscillations occur at but a single frequency, it is said to be coherent, and it is perceived as a single color of extreme purity. What the laser does is to produce such light of great intensity.

Though not generally realized, virtually all visible light is

A continuous-wave krypton laser produces a steady beam of coherent light which is segregated by a prism into beams of red, blue, and green light.

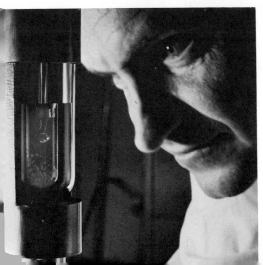

Dr. Jacques Pankove examines the intense coherent red light being emitted from a gallium-arsenide, semiconductor laser. The unit is housed in a standard transistor case and immersed in liquid nitrogen.

produced by the electron. Moreover, there are only three known ways by which it performs this unique feat. The first is by gaining so much energy that it can move through a substance, such as water, faster than light (which moves much more slowly in solids and liquids than in space). In that case, it generates a bright electromagnetic wake called *Cerenkov radiation,* a phenomenon commonly associated with certain types of nuclear reactors that are submerged in water to trap their radioactivity.

A second way is for the electron to be continuously accelerated at high speed (as when it is forced to orbit around a magnetic field) producing *cyclotron radiation* or to be rapidly decelerated (as when it is captured or nearly captured by an atom) producing a light called *bremsstrahlung,* a phenomenon associated with high-temperature plasmas and a process for generating x-rays. Both effects are considered to be different sides of the same coin.

The third, and most useful way by far, is for an electron orbiting a stable atom to receive a sudden push from an outside electric, magnetic, or combined electromagnetic field. If this push is sufficiently strong, the electron will jump to a higher orbit in the atom, tarry there for a time, and then collapse back to its original level, shucking off its excess energy in the form of light. Depending on how long it takes this cycle to occur, we call the process incandescence, fluorescence, or phosphorescence.

Electrons not only produce light, however. They also respond to it. For example, when electrons of certain materials connected in an electrical circuit are struck by light, they spring away from their parent atoms and proceed to wander through the material, causing an electric current to flow. This is the mechanism of photoconductivity. Or, electrons subjected to light in still other materials may absorb so much energy that they jump out of their parent atoms and out of their host material altogether to become available for work in free space. Such is the mechanism of photoemission.

Generator, detector, converter, amplifier, and plaything of light beams, the *electron,* through electronics science, is leading man inexorably on to a still newer age in which power, communications, and computer information will be packaged in photons and ported through space on bright, impalpable electromagnetic rays.

Dr. F. H. Nicoll observes output of an electron-beam pumped zinc oxide laser. Instead of coming out as a beam, the ultraviolet light of the laser comes out in a 360° plane.

CHAPTER 19

Lasers

On May 9, 1962, a team of research scientists at MIT led by Dr. Louis Smullin and including Glenn Hardway, an engineer from the Raytheon Company, made final adjustments to a complex of optical and electronic instruments set up on the campus grounds. They checked their watches and waited, eyeing the pale half-moon that cast a brazen glow over the scene. At last, the word came. One of the scientists touched a button, and instantly, a flash of intense red light shot upward, briefly etching its path in a layer of unsuspected haze as it raced toward the moon.

Three seconds later, it had burst on the lunar surface, southeast of the crater Albategnius, and had been reflected back to

MIT, where its return was duly noted in the sensitive photo-multipliers of a telescopic receiver. For the first time in history, man had built a light strong enough to illuminate a celestial body.

As it turns out, the light beam that made this unprecedented 478,000-mile round trip was emitted from a 6-inch ruby rod, no thicker than a lead pencil. This ruby comprised the heart of a new electronic device called a *laser*.

Able to amplify light waves, just as radio waves are amplified, lasers foreshadow an era in which light beams may be used to guide space vehicles, communicate between planets, perform delicate eye and brain surgery, weld and machine difficult metals, destroy hostile missiles in flight, and detect enemy submarines hovering near the ocean floor.

Right now, for example, scientists and electronics engineers are perfecting a laser radar for battlefield use, a laser tracking system for monitoring the flight performance of United States missiles, a laser computer whose circuits may operate, literally, at the speed of light, and a laser recorder that can produce high resolution images, drawings, or printed texts on photographic film. Also, they are deeply engaged in developing laser communications systems which, in theory, could use a beam of light to carry all the radio, television, and telephone traffic currently transmitted throughout the world.

The word "laser" is derived from a phrase that describes the device's function: *l*ight *a*mplification by *s*timulated *e*mission of *r*adiation. Ideally, lasers amplify light in the same way that a great river, such as the Mississippi, can be said to amplify its many tributaries into one immensely powerful body of water. Ordinary light is composed of all the colors in the visible and near-visible spectrum. Lasers take these frequency components of ordinary light and convert them into a single, powerful frequency of enormous purity.

One mechanism by which this conversion is accomplished

may be found in a semi-transparent crystal containing atoms that can be made to fluoresce. Chromium or the so-called rare earths are examples of such atoms. When the crystal is exposed to an intense light source, certain electrons orbiting the nuclei of these atoms gain enough energy to jump into a higher orbit. Here, however, they are unstable and fall back to their original orbit, giving up their newly acquired energy primarily in the form of light.

Essentially, all fluorescent materials work this way, but in the laser, this process is rigidly controlled so that most of the electrons emit light of exactly the same energy and frequency. Therefore, these independent emissions add together to form a coherent beam so intense that, when focused, it will melt any known material instantly. Because of this coherence, incidentally, laser beams travel in straight lines over enormous distances without spreading appreciably. This explains why MIT was able to perform its historic moon experiment.

It was in 1958 that the first proposal for constructing a solid-state laser was made in a scientific paper published by Dr. Charles H. Townes, while at Columbia University, and Dr. Arthur L. Schawlow, of Bell Telephone Laboratories. Both men held that electrons, in the proper environment, could be made to emit light in a predictable and controllable way.

The knowledge that electrons can emit light was not new. Certain crystals exposed to ultraviolet radiation, fluorescent lamps, even television screens give off electron-emitted light. What was new in this proposal was that such light might be made coherent.

It was not until June, 1960, however, that Dr. Maiman announced achievement of the first solid-state laser. The unit, a ruby crystal, worked like a gun and fired pulses of intense red light when activated by a brilliant xenon flash lamp. Unfortunately, these pulses were extremely brief—less than a thousandth of a second long—and their great power could not be sustained long enough to do much useful work. Even so, this and similar instruments are being used today in efforts to generate harmonics from red light, to achieve light beams of unbelievable energy, and to study the very nature of light itself.

In December, 1960, International Business Machines, Inc., reported building a laser similar to the Maiman device but using a calcium fluoride crystal containing trace atoms of uranium.

In February, 1961, still another group, this one led by Ali Javan at Bell Telephone Laboratories, announced a totally new kind of laser—one that used gases instead of solids. Even more important, this laser, employing a mixture of helium and neon, was activated by an electrical discharge, instead of a flash lamp, and emitted light continuously instead of in pulses. Its power was strictly limited, however.

In this heady atmosphere, an RCA research team, under the direction of Dr. Henry R. Lewis, began searching for ways to make dramatically improved lasers. They decided to enlist the help of a materials research group directed by Dr. Simon Larach.

In October, 1961, the first breakthrough occurred. Dr. Larach and his associates succeeded in pioneering an advanced method for growing calcium fluoride crystals of high-optical quality.

The next big hurdle was to find a fluorescent material to use in these crystals. The need was for a substance that would absorb all the wavelengths of visible light and then fluoresce in only one color—the purer the better. The rare earths suggested themselves immediately. However, there are fourteen such elements, and the question arose as to which ones would make the best lasers. In the absence of a clear-cut answer, Dr. Larach's group began the herculean task of preparing calcium fluoride crystals individually diffused with all the rare earths, with the exception of promethium which is radioactive.

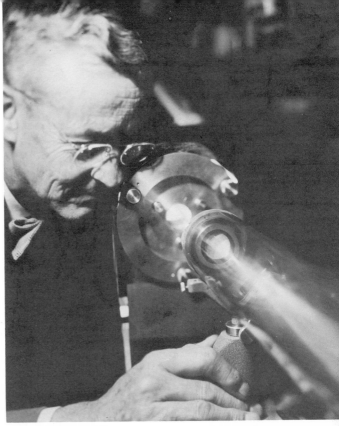

Orville Dow focuses output of a helium-neon laser
inside a tube of smoke in order to study the spectral
character of the beam.

John McCormack aligns lenses
and mirrors of an optical
interferometer.

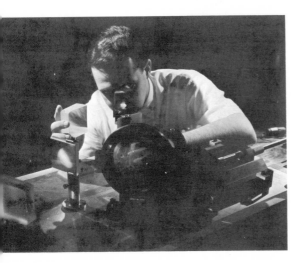

In the meantime, Dr. Lewis and others sought a better understanding of laser action and a more precise knowledge of the forces at work within laser crystals. In this pursuit he turned to a coworker, Dr. Donald McClure, a specialist in atomic and electronic interactions in crystals, now at the University of Chicago. Dr. McClure provided the key that opened the way to a second breakthrough.

In Dr. McClure's view, the more promising fluorescent materials to use were not simply rare earths but divalent rare earths—rare earth atoms lacking two electrons in their outer orbits. Divalent rare earths, he reasoned, would not only absorb more incoming light energy in the visible range but, by their nature, could also be expected to emit far more light.

The importance of this hypothesis can be appreciated when it is realized that crystal lasers reported up to this time had many serious drawbacks. They were notoriously inefficient. Only one one-thousandth of the total energy poured into them was being converted to light. The rest was going into heat.

Furthermore, enormous energy was required to make them work. The flash lamps used to trigger them had to radiate thousands of watts. The reason lay in the inability of the reported lasers to use all of the light frequencies available from the lamps. To derive sufficient energy from the few they were using, therefore, it was necessary to raise the incoming frequencies to as high a power as practicable. Dr. McClure's suggestion seemed to offer a solution to both difficulties.

Subsequent studies of the rare earths showed that two—thulium and dysprosium—offered, in divalent form, the best combination of fluorescent, thermal, and structural features needed for laser action. Unfortunately, both were trivalent in their natural state—that is, they were lacking three rather than two electrons in their outer orbit.

Putting an electron back into this orbit was the next challenge. The problem was one of chemistry, and Dr. Larach was again consulted. After several months of unsuccessful experiments, his staff found a solution. By January, 1962, RCA had all the ingredients for a new laser.

At this juncture, Bell Telephone Laboratories announced the development of a solid-state laser that generated coherent infrared light continuously. The device employed a calcium tungstate crystal containing trace atoms of the rare earth neodymium. Bell had also departed from use of a xenon flash lamp and had resorted, instead, to an equally powerful mercury lamp that shone continuously.

In the first week of April, 1962, RCA reported its new laser —a calcium fluoride crystal laced with divalent dysprosium that emitted intense pulses of infrared light when activated by a xenon flash lamp. Shortly thereafter, a mercury lamp was substituted, and the laser was made to operate continuously. Ultimately, this laser proved to be so efficient, in fact, that it could be operated from nothing more than focused sunlight, and it became the first *sun-pumped* laser ever reported.

Subsequently, in October of the same year, still another milestone in laser technology was passed with the simultaneous development by Marshall Nathan, at IBM, and Robert Hall, at General Electric, of the world's first *injection* lasers. These differed from the earlier light-pumped and gas-discharge types in that they were semiconductor diodes—tiny crystals of gallium arsenide containing a single junction from which a flat ray of coherent infrared light emerged when an electric current possessing a certain critical density passed through it.

The achievement of the laser, in all its forms, marks a high point in the theory and practice of modern electronics. It has united optical and electronic phenomena in new and compelling ways that are clearly destined to revolutionize our lives in the years ahead.

An experimental liquid-crystal clock driven by a transistor circuit is compared for accuracy with a standard, mechanically driven wrist watch. The scientist is Dr. Robert Lohman.

CHAPTER 20

The
Ostentatious
Electron

After 130 years of harnessing light indirectly, for the most part by converting it first to electrical phenomena—solar cells and television cameras are good examples—electronics scientists are making an audacious bid to gain direct electronic control over the electromagnetic properties of light.

Using a felicitous farrago of new electronic materials and novel, though obscure, effects, they are presently training light to drill holes in diamond dies, to carry radio and TV signals, to align tunnel-boring equipment, to track earth satellites, to provide inertial guidance for missiles, and to produce optical memory and logic circuits for computers. In the process, they are also fashioning a new optoelectronics technology, more aptly dubbed *op electronics*.

Nowhere are the potential benefits of this developing technology more evident, however, than in the area of visible displays where a series of recent breakthroughs promises to revolutionize everything from wristwatches and automotive dashboards to computer readout, television screens, and phonograph records.

In its strictest sense, of course, op electronics is not new. It derives originally, as we have seen, from the work of Julius Plücker, who, in 1859, discovered the phenomenon of *cathodoluminescence*—that light is given off when certain phosphors are struck by beams of electrons—(called *cathode rays* in Plücker's day, hence the name).

Several years later, in 1897, Ferdinand Braun, also in Germany, employed this and other discoveries to build the first cathode-ray oscilloscope—a vacuum tube that produced a beam of electrons that could be deflected up, down, or sideways by exterior magnets and that featured a phosphor screen on which movements of the beam could be followed by watching the bright spot it created. Among the descendants of this ingenious tube, presently, are the laboratory oscilloscope for observing high-speed electrical phenomena, the radarscope for monitoring the flight of airplanes and missiles, and the kinescope for displaying images received by the ubiquitous TV set.

Thus, the Braun tube was the first practical optoelectronic device and still serves, years later, as the technological touchstone—even inspiration—of many of the modern efforts being made to surpass it and its kith. This is especially true in those cases where the only change contemplated is in the substitution of a new material for the phosphor screen invariably found at the viewing end of most display tubes.

Three such changes, which have been proposed and demonstrated experimentally, are very exciting and might even prove revolutionary, should they become practical. The first involves use of a screen composed of lasers of a remarkable cathodoluminescent type—tiny crystalline flakes of such materials as cadmium sulfide or zinc oxide—that can be activated or "pumped" by an electron beam of sufficient energy and that emit intense, coherent light in a flat, 360° halo whose edge remains extremely narrow over relatively long distances.

By substituting these lasers for the phosphors in a conventional TV screen, Dr. Frederick Nicoll, of RCA Laboratories, hopes to produce a bright visual display that can be viewed directly or be intensified still further for projection onto a distant wall or movie screen. He has already built and successfully operated an experimental tube, containing several such lasers in a row, and plans to add still more in the future. Eventually, a tube with a full row of such lasers might even be used as a kind of *flying spot scanner*—a device like the one employed by the lunar orbiter satellites to convert film of the moon's surface to television signals for relay to earth.

A second approach of equal scientific panache and far-reaching applications potential is that involving the use of a photochromic instead of a phosphor screen. Since the invention of paint and the development of clothing dyes, it has been known that certain of these materials become bleached or undergo color changes when exposed to sunlight for varying periods. In our own day, as a matter of fact, clothing shops, fabric barns, and furniture stores often employ awnings or tinted glass to protect their showrooms from some or all of the solar frequencies—primarily those in the ultraviolet range—which are known to be responsible for such alterations.

Although virtually everyone has experienced these subtle, often exasperating effects at one time or another (housewives even take advantage of them by hanging white laundry out to be both dried and bleached by the sun), it was not until very recently that anyone undertook to determine precisely what atomic mechanisms are involved in producing them. Ironically, it was unwanted and deleterious bleaching occurring in a crystal laser—RCA's famous *sun-pumped* type announced in 1962—that triggered such investigations.

This laser, built by Dr. Zoltan Kiss, was a single crystal of calcium fluoride containing traces of the rare earth dysprosium and could be activated either by exposure to sunlight or by intense radiance from a mercury vapor lamp. Unfortunately, as it turned out, this type of illumination bleached the material and steadily degraded its performance. At first concerned with counteracting the effect, which ultimately proved possible, Dr. Kiss soon became engrossed with trying to exploit it instead. Finally, after an exhaustive series of analytical studies, he was able to show that the dysprosium atoms—which were responsible for the laser action—contained electrons that slowly leaked from their outermost orbits into defects in the surrounding crystal. As a result, the atoms were becoming absorbers of the very light they were supposed to emit.

Since these crystal defects, or *electron traps,* as they are called, could not be controlled or easily eliminated, Dr. Kiss decided to add traces of a second rare earth, europium, to the crystal. He reasoned that the atoms of this material would have greater affinity than the defects for the electrons being lost by the atoms of the first rare earth and would enhance the photochromic effect as well. For similar reasons, he also changed the original rare earth from dysprosium to samarium. Happily, the stratagem worked! Not only that, but he found further that the bleaching, or discoloration, produced when light of one frequency kicked electrons from the samarium to the europium atoms, could be reversed by light of another frequency which tended to kick the electrons back again, returning the material as a whole to its original state and hue. Therefore, by using outside light of at least two distinct frequencies or colors, he found he could produce a kind of atomic "ping-pong game"

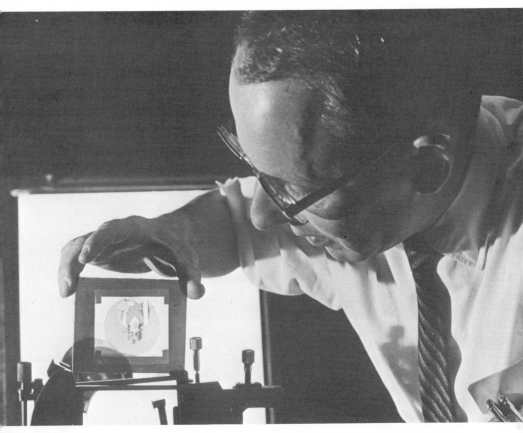

A black-and-white transparency containing color information in the form of phase differences (wavelength position and direction) is inserted into a holder between a light source and a diffraction grating. Phase differences in the transparency now create phase differences in the light passing through. These, in turn, become color differences when the light passes through the diffraction grating, and a full-color image is reproduced.

An experimental liquid-crystal display that could be used as a fuel gauge or speedometer is shown. Bars on array become reflective when activated by certain predetermined electric voltages.

Dr. Joel Goldmacher pours two different liquid crystals together—one nematic, the other cholesteric—to produce a unique liquid-crystal cell (black square) that can be turned on and will remain in the "on" state even with the power off.

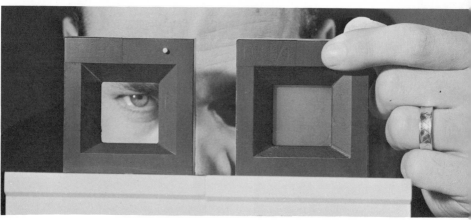

RCA scientist demonstrates two liquid-crystal cells. The clear one, on the left, has not been turned on. The one on the right has been turned on with the result that it has become totally reflective.

within the crystal that could be the basis for "writing" and "erasing" information on a photochromic surface.

In subsequent studies, he even determined that such writing could be accomplished on one side of the material by an electron beam and, if the material were thin enough, erased by light on the other. Thus was born the *cathodochromic* electron tube—an experimental device with a photochromic instead of a phosphor screen. Its great advantage is that it can be written on by standard television techniques and can retain its pictures or data up to a half hour, even when the tube is turned off. This makes it especially well suited for the display of data that change periodically—airline departure and arrival schedules, stock transactions and last sales, parimutuel odds, and the like. Moreover, data displayed in this way can be altered or updated from outside or be erased entirely by a light pen, laser beam, or other source of illumination.

A third candidate for replacing phosphors in the screens of TV tubes is the *nematic liquid crystal*. The liquid-crystal state, or phase, as it is called, is a transition, or twilight zone, that occurs in many organic compounds somewhere between their solid and completely liquid states. Materials in this phase possess not only the mechanical properties of a liquid (they flow) but the optical properties of a polycrystalline solid. Ergo, their name.

This condition was first identified in 1888 when an Austrian botanist by the name of Friedrich Reinitzer found that certain organic compounds he was investigating did not melt cleanly. Thereafter, others found that there are three types of liquid crystals: a *smectic* variety whose molecules arrange themselves vertically, like cans of soup stacked atop each other on a supermarket shelf; the *cholesteric* types whose molecules are laid out horizontally but are stacked in helical fashion, like steps in a winding staircase; and the *nematic* brand whose molecules are also laid out horizontally but are stacked, like stick matches in a box. All of these architectural arrangements, it develops, are due to Van der Waals forces—weak electrical attractions between the molecules—whose existence won their discoverer, Johannes van der Waals, the Nobel Prize in 1910. Still later, in 1931, a German chemist by the name of Wilhelm Kast found that liquid-crystal molecules can be forced to line up in an electric field.

Such intriguing features were bound to capture the attention of electronics scientists sooner or later and, in the mid-1960s, impelled Dr. George Heilmeier, of RCA Laboratories, to believe it might be possible to use such materials to achieve all-electronic displays of a novel, reflective type. Starting with materials that exhibited nematic behavior only within a narrow temperature range of 90 to about 110°C, he and his research

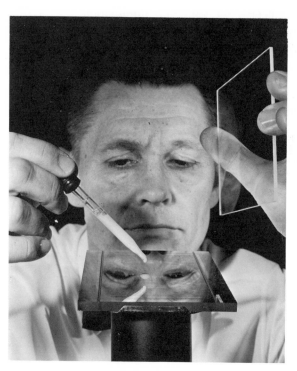

Dr. Lucian Barton squeezes a drop of liquid-crystal material onto reflective glass plate. Transparent plate in his other hand will then be placed over the first to form a liquid-crystal display panel.

team made their first important discovery: that when a film of usually transparent material was trapped between two plates of glass and subjected to a small electric voltage, it instantly became opaque. Ions—in this case, electrically charged molecules generated in the film by the voltage—were moving from one of the glass plates to the other, disrupting the orderly molecular arrangements of the liquid crystal, and causing it to scatter rather than transmit light. In fact, the higher the voltage, up to a certain limit, the more the scattering.

Next, Heilmeier's team went to work on the temperature problem. Could a nematic material be found or fabricated that would have a wider temperature range? After several months of trial and error and of patient chemistry, a second important discovery was made. It was possible to produce a material whose liquid-crystal state could be maintained over a range from below freezing to the boiling point of water.

Proof of this nematic pudding was obtained several months later when Dr. John Van Raalte, also of RCA Laboratories, succeeded in building a tube with a small liquid-crystal screen that could be scanned by an electron beam, in the conventional manner, and could receive and display standard broadcast pictures. These differed from ordinary TV pictures only in that they were seen by reflected light from their surroundings (in the same way a printed page is seen) rather than by light which they themselves emitted, as in the case of phosphors.

As indicated by Dr. Heilmeier's original discovery, however, it is not necessary to use an electron beam to activate a liquid-crystal screen. A simple electric field produced between two electrodes is sufficient to make it scatter light. If one or both of these electrodes are transparent—tin oxide is ideal as such an electrode—it is possible to produce flat displays for use as the face of an all-electronic watch, a speedometer or other dashboard instrument, a silent cash register or desk calculator, an alphanumeric readout, and the like. It might even make pos-

sible a flat television display one day, though this "consumma-
tion devoutly to be wished" requires more than just a flat
screen. It also requires some means, other than an electron
beam, of lightening or darkening about 250,000 points on the
screen every second—the number of "bits," roughly, that make
up a standard TV picture.

Cathodoluminescent or electron-beam-pumped lasers, photochromic materials, liquid crystals—all figure prominently in the
effort to achieve new forms of electronic displays based on the
way certain materials generate, absorb, or reflect light. Still
other electronic displays are being worked on, however, that
depend upon how certain materials transmit light. Some of the
most dramatic of these use lasers as their source of light and
use mosaics of tiny electrooptical or magnetooptical "windows"
to produce rapid intensity changes at various points in the laser
beams as they pass through on their way to a distant screen.

Such systems are based upon the fact that the electric and
magnetic fields, which make up light, vibrate both vertically
and horizontally as they propagate through space. Furthermore, it turns out that the electric field in this partnership can
always be resolved, at any instant in time, into two right-angle
components, much like the cross hairs in a bomb sight. Finally,
because of the way these vertical and horizontal components
interact with certain transparent materials, it is possible to
suppress one of them (to polarize the light) as the light passes
through or to change its orientation (to change the plane of
the light's polarization). Some materials do this naturally by
virtue of the way they are constructed. Others do so only when
subjected to an electric or magnetic field.

Focusing on this latter category, scientists have now fash-
ioned materials from which they are able to build tiny
mullioned windows whose optical characteristics can be altered electronically and in any pattern so that as light passes
through them their action is combined to produce a sort of

electrooptical or magnetooptical transparency that can be projected directly onto a screen.

To the standard television technique of producing images by controlling the emission of light from an array of phosphors, scientists are now adding an extraordinary ability to produce these same images by controlling the absorption, reflection, and even transmission of light by other, more exotic materials. In the process, they are paving the way for a pantheon of new products built on the optoelectronic antics of the ostentatious electron.

Macy Heller appears to grasp a molecular model which is really a three-dimensional reconstruction (the virtual image) of a transmission hologram.

CHAPTER 21

Holography

In a feat of cryptography as stunning, in its way, as the breaking of the Japanese diplomatic code on the eve of World War II, scientists have succeeded in cracking the phase code of light. Using the laser as an electromagnetic Rosetta Stone, they have developed a new kind of photography that makes it possible to record an object or scene in all its colors and in all three dimensions. Not only that, but the resulting image, when viewed from various angles, undergoes all the optical permutations associated with a scene viewed through a window. For instance, the background blurs when the eye is focused on the foreground, and vice versa; objects behind structures in the foreground pop into sight when the viewing angle is changed;

the entire scene continues to be visible even when part or most of it is covered, just as it does when a shade is pulled halfway down.

Dubbed *holography*, from the Greek meaning to record everything, this new technology has already led the nation's major research laboratories to assemble small guerrilla bands of mathematicians, physicists, and specialists in optics to conduct spoiling raids across its frontiers in search of new understanding and new applications of light.

From these forays eventually may come three-dimensional color movies and, possibly, TV, neither of which will require special glasses to be viewed; three-dimensional photographs and paintings that hang on the wall and occupy no more space than the two-dimensional versions; computer memories that store information in the form of light patterns registered not only on the surfaces of certain materials but in their bulk as well; devices that can store ultrasonic sound patterns in such a way that they can be read out with light after they have been used to "photograph" the interior organs of the body; other devices that can record x-rays and be read out with visible light in a magnification process which may make it possible to see atomic structure in three dimensions, for the first time; new optical instruments for measuring air pollution in volume, for performing remarkably accurate analyses of objects under stress, and for doing contour mapping. The list of possible applications of holography grows longer and more fantastic every day.

The product of holography—called a *hologram*—is usually a large glass slide which is either completely transparent or slightly hazy. If hazy, further investigation under a high-powered microscope reveals that one side of the hologram has a peculiar graininess, consisting of dark and light ripples, scattered through it in ostensibly random fashion.

These curious graffiti are actually frozen into a photographic emulsion which has been exposed directly to an object illuminated by a laser, without the intervention of a lens. Since even the eye sees nothing but a blur without its natural lens, it is not surprising that the emulsion contains no recognizable image. What it does contain is a record, in the form of microscopic particles of precipitated silver (produced via the same chemistry that makes conventional negatives), of where the varying intensities of light reflected from the object fell upon it.

It contains one thing more. Within these markings is a record of where this reflected light interfered with light coming directly to the emulsion from the same laser. It is the interference in a photographic emulsion or other photosensitive material of the direct and reflected laser light that gives rise to the unusual properties of holograms.

The phenomenon of optical interference—the reason why oil slicks and soap bubbles often display rich color patterns on their surfaces—was first explained by the British physicist Thomas Young in 1801. It occurs because light energy propagates through space in the form of electromagnetic waves.

If, for some reason, some of the waves fall behind their comrades so that their peaks occur in the troughs between the others, they cancel each other, in a process known as *destructive interference*. It is this effect, incidentally, that is responsible for the shadows that appear behind objects illuminated from the front. It is also the reason why light seems not to go around corners, like sound or water waves. Actually it does, but its waves are so short that, on passing an edge, they begin to interfere with and cancel each other in the incredibly short distance of only one wavelength—about the distance through the limpid rind of a bulbous soap bubble.

If, on the other hand, such electromagnetic waves fall so far behind that they find themselves in step with the wave following them—like a parade soldier who has fallen back to the next row of marchers—they add their energy to the new one, in a process called *constructive interference*.

In the case of ordinary light, the electromagnetic waves are a mob of different frequencies and intensities jostling each other as they advance, like the clutter of waves on the surface of the ocean. Thus, they are always interfering with each other in a way that changes from moment to moment.

In the case of laser light, however, the waves are completely synchronized in a parade march whose wavefronts advance in perfect rhythm and with uniform intensity, like rows of soldiers passing a reviewing stand. Thus, they never interfere with each other unless they are made to do so. It is the fact that they can be made to do so selectively and in a way that does not change with time which is the basis of holography.

A laser beam is generated and split into two beams. The first is directed at an object to be holographed, while the second is sent directly to a photographic plate. Upon reflection from the object, the first undergoes intensity and phase changes which the second—the reference beam—does not. When the two meet again in the photographic emulsion, therefore, they interfere, and a hologram is born.

What this really means is that, in addition to recording the average intensity of the reflected laser light, the hologram also records the directions in which the individual light waves were moving at the time they struck the emulsion. The latter information is registered in the emulsion in the form of an extremely fine-grained interference pattern composed of silver particles precipitated in varying densities.

To read the hologram out, after it is developed, and to produce the three-dimensional image latent within it, it is only necessary to pass a laser beam of the same frequency as the original back through it. At a certain angle the pattern of silver particles distributed throughout the emulsion breaks up the laser beam into individual waves that exactly correspond to those which were reflected from the object originally. It is something like using a record to make a phonograph needle vibrate in order to produce sound of the same frequency as

A reflection hologram produces the real and conjugate image of a photographic transparency. The images are intercepted by frosted glass slides.

that which made the stylus vibrate when the sound was first recorded.

Although holograms of complete images are new, holograms of single points of light go back to 1818 when the great French physicist Augustin Fresnel demonstrated what has since come to be known as the Fresnel *zone plate*. This is a glass plate on which narrowly spaced concentric circles have been scribed in accordance with a highly precise formula. As a result, when an ordinary light beam of a single color passes through it, the beam undergoes constructive and destructive interference in such a way that a point of light can be seen to hover behind the plate in space, if an observer looks through it toward the light beam. Thus, a modern hologram is really many Fresnel zone plates, superimposed so each produces its own point of light at its own unique focus and all add together to form an image.

Even the idea of producing images—and vivid colors—by using the phenomenon of light interference is not new. It was first conceived by William Zenker, of Berlin, in 1868, and first demonstrated by the French photographer Gabriel Lippmann in 1891. What Lippmann did was to use a thin, transparent emulsion on a glass slide backed by a shiny surface of mercury. When light waves from an object to be photographed penetrated the emulsion and were reflected back by the mercury, they met and interfered with others just entering the emulsion. (This is exactly how an oil slick on water produces the interference colors we associate with it.) The result was a series of interference patterns trapped in the emulsion. These could be made to reproduce full, two-dimensional color images by the simple expedient of shining a strong white light on them at the proper angle. In fact, Lippmann photographs were the first true color photographs ever made from life.

Once again, in 1934, the principle of light interference set the world abuzz with the development of the phase-contrast

The optical "forest" through which a laser beam must run on its way to producing a hologram.

microscope by Frits Zernike in Holland. For years, the study of biological specimens—human tissue, microbes, and other organic material—had been impeded by the fact that they were almost completely transparent to the microscope's eye. Zernike found, however, that if the light being used were split so that a portion went through the specimen and another portion went through a transparent piece of mica, the two got out of phase and interfered when they were brought back together. The result was a high-contrast microscope for use in biological research for the first time. In 1953, Zernike won the Nobel Prize for this work.

The next major development in the use of interference phenomena was Dennis Gabor's concept of three-dimensional holographic imaging, propounded at the Imperial College of Science and Technology in London, in 1947. He hoped to use the wave nature of electrons to create electron interference patterns from which he could reconstruct magnified images by optical rather than by electronic means. Unfortunately, he could not get the necessary coherence in the electron beam. There things remained until 1960 and the development of the first laser.

Seizing on this development and improving on the concepts of Gabor by introducing the idea of a reference beam to create interference, Emmett Leith and Juris Upatnieks, working with a gas laser at the University of Michigan in 1962, produced the first hologram to give three-dimensional images. The scientific world has not been quite the same since.

Today, there is scarcely an electronics research laboratory not investigating the subject. Scientists are exploring everything from the feasibility of hologram computer memories that store information in three dimensions, to hologram movies, and holograms whose images could be magnified in all three dimensions at the same time to father a whole new type of optical microscopy.

Their major aim at the moment, however, is to gain new and fundamental insight into the phenomenon of holography itself. In that connection, they have produced several novel forms of hologram: phase holograms that record three-dimensional information on a mirror surface that is read by reflection; holograms whose images are read out in only two dimensions, like conventional photographs but with the difference that such "snapshots" are only one twenty-fifth of an inch on a side; and holograms that store not one but many images. Soon they plan to produce an improved white-light hologram—one made in laser light but one that can be read in ordinary daylight, or in other words, a kind of Lippmann photograph in three dimensions.

The ability of holograms to produce standard photographs rests on the fact that they can be made to reconstruct two types of three-dimensional images: one, the so-called *virtual image,* appears only when you look through the hologram in the general direction of the readout laser beam; the other, called the *real image,* is seen on the other side of the hologram and may be recorded in two dimensions by simply inserting a screen or photographic plate in the path of the light.

The ability to produce color holograms in three dimensions which are visible in ordinary light depends on a surprising technique that employs the thickness of the hologram emulsion itself. Different colored lasers—red, blue, and green—all illuminate the object to be holographed at the same time. The reference beam of each, instead of hitting the front side where the reflected beam is received, is directed to the back of the hologram. As a consequence, the interference patterns created by each are much finer and lie much closer together. If white light is now shone through the back surface of such a hologram, a full-color reconstruction of the virtual image results. This happens because the hologram acts as a color filter—it allows through only those frequencies composing the white light that are close to the ones used to record the image in the first place. So far, such holograms have shown certain drawbacks, however—they are somewhat dim, and their colors are usually distorted.

With the invention of standard contrast photography by Louis Daguerre in 1839, man found a way to record chemically two-thirds of the graphic information encoded in light reflected from an object. Now, with the invention of holography, he has found a way to record the other third. In the process, his ability to investigate and to portray the world around him has acquired—both literally and figuratively—a brand new dimension.

Key texts that embody the theories and principles of modern electronics are displayed along with written formulas and a statuette of Rodin's "The Thinker."

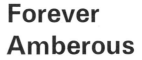

CHAPTER 22

Forever Amberous

Electrical and magnetic phenomena, as such, have been recognized for at least twenty-six centuries, but their source, their interrelationships, and their infinite capacity for reforming the human condition and reshaping human society have been largely unknown until current times.

Only in the past 100 years, for example, has man learned that these two forces constitute aspects of a single, electromagnetic "sea" that surrounds, inundates, and permeates all of mankind. Moreover, unlike its terrestrial counterparts, this sea has no shoreline save the edges of the universe itself, and its bottom, though approached in recent nuclear studies, has yet to be sounded.

Nevertheless, man is learning to use it at an ever-accelerating rate. The dynamo and the battery; the electron tube, the transistor, the laser; the wired circuit, the printed circuit, the integrated circuit; the telephone, the phonograph, the radio, the television set; the analog and the digital computer—such are the dams and storage towers, the pumps, valves, plumbing, faucets, and other components already developed to tap and harness it. Much more is on the way, however, in line with an effort to develop:

communications, radar, and data processing systems that employ the much higher electromagnetic frequencies of millimeter, submillimeter, infrared, and optical wavelengths in order to handle more information per second than ever before.

the automation of instruments and controls with all sensors, counters, switches, readouts and shutoffs linked to a computer and under direct digital control.

machines whose enormous processing speeds and memory capacity will lead to a form of artificial intelligence that will be employed directly to accept data, render low-level decisions, and take action without the intercession of human beings.

the increasing integration of electronic functions in man-made crystals whose character will begin to take on the semblance of "living material" systems, capable of many diverse and simultaneous electronic activities.

the creation and use of exotic material complexes and of strange states of matter to achieve unprecedented electronic effects such as room-temperature superconductivity.

the conversion of all forms of energy—mechanical, acoustical, optical, even nuclear—to electrical energy and back again to the same or other forms, in order to achieve smaller, more efficient, and more versatile electronic systems.

the conversion of other types of energy directly to electric power, free of transmission wires, gasoline engines, steam boilers, and other mechanical contrivances.

the exploitation of organic materials, such as liquid crystals, and greater use of the gaseous and liquid states of matter, as in certain types of lasers, to achieve cheaper and more flexible electronic devices.

These are some of the more prominent and promising trends that can be descried at present. But their meaning, as well as the directions in which they are taking man, can be seen best only by placing them in perspective and against a background of electronic discovery, research, and invention that goes back to ancient Greece.

Amber was the first clue to the existence of electricity, as lodestone was to magnetism. The former is a root-beer colored substance—the fossilized remnant of gums and resins exuded by prehistoric pines—which caught the notice of the Greek philosopher Thales about 640 B.C. because it attracted bits of linen and certain other materials, when rubbed. After considerable meditation on the subject, Thales concluded that the stuff was alive and exerted its attraction by a process akin to inhaling. Although lodestone seemed somewhat different—it could pass its "life force" on to other materials, such as iron, by rendering them magnetic also—he felt it, too, partook of the same general nature as amber. There the subject rested for the next 1,800 years.

Then in 1214, Roger Bacon, an enterprising bureaucrat in the service of the British Crown and a man of great intellectual force and scientific flair, reopened the subject once again. The peculiar powers of amber and lodestone were certainly not the result of their being alive, he felt. With all due respect to Mr. Thales, there must be a better explanation.

Some fifty-five years later, on a French battlefield near Anjou, a one-time crusader by the name of Peter Peregrinus de Maricourt noticed that a disk-shaped piece of lodestone—a *terrella,* or "little earth," as he called it—had two different areas of magnetism. He promptly called these poles, and a few years later, in 1600, Sir William Gilbert, physician to Queen Elizabeth I, followed his lead and concluded that the earth itself is a magnet. Thereafter, nothing new was heard about magnetism until 1820.

Not so in the case of amber. Once Jerome Cardan, the Italian mathematician and inventor, had clearly stated, in 1576, the differences between the properties of lodestone and amber—the differences, in effect, between magnetism and electricity—several researchers got to work on the latter. By the mid-seventeenth century, a host of new materials had been found that showed properties akin to those of amber. For a time, these were referred to as *electrics* (after *elektron,* the Greek word for amber), and before long, the property itself came to be called electricity. By the end of the century, in fact, several machines using electrics had been built, and substantial charges of static electricity were being generated regularly to frighten or amuse family and friends.

Such electrical fun-and-games continued well into the eighteenth century, although they became more elaborate with the discovery in 1729, by the Englishman Stephen Gray, that electricity will flow in a conductor (he used a piece of hempen string); with the discovery of *capacitance* in 1745, by Pieter van Musschenbroek, in Holland (he invented the Leyden jar which trapped a very big charge between a moist hand and the water held in an insulating glass container); with Charles Dufay's discovery in France, in 1740, that there are two types of electricity (what Benjamin Franklin soon after called *posi-*

tive and *negative charges*); with Luigi Galvani's portentous find, in 1786, that electricity will activate or galvanize animal muscles (he used a frog's legs); and with Count Alessandro Volta's invention of the battery in 1794 (it worked, but not for the reasons he gave).

A note of greater seriousness was struck in the following century, however. On May 2, 1800, for example, William Nicholson and Anthony Carlisle, working in England, found they could break down water into two gases, hydrogen and oxygen, by passing an electric current through it. Thus was the modern theory of chemistry born, for this experiment immediately led a countryman, Sir Humphry Davy, to apply the same procedure to potash and salt with the result that he discovered and isolated magnesium and sodium. A protégé of Davy's, Michael Faraday, then conceived the idea that chemical compounds are held together by the attraction of positive and negative electric charges which can be broken up, in some cases, by the passage of electric currents or through the agency of certain solutions. The positive charges he called *ions,* and the solutions he called *electrolytes.*

An equally astonishing discovery was that of Hans Christian Oersted, in Holland twenty years later, when he noticed that the needle of a compass, placed close to an electric wire by mere chance, swung sideways whenever the current was on. He had found the long-sought connection between electricity and magnetism! An electric current generates a magnetic field at right angles to its flow. Not long after, the electromagnet—a solid iron cylinder wrapped with hundreds of turns of insulated electric wire—was devised and has since found its greatest popular usage in ringing doorbells and telephones.

Once this connection had been made, it did not take very long for Joseph Henry, in America, and Michael Faraday, in England, to wonder if the magnetic field generated by an electric current flowing in one wire would induce an electric current to flow in a parallel wire by means of its associated magnetic field. Subsequently, about 1831, they both independently discovered the principle of electromagnetic induction—the principle on which the modern electric-power industry is founded. Henry even went further to discover the principle of inductance by which the magnetic field generated by an electric current tends to induce a countercurrent to its own flow and thus to oppose itself.

Momentous as all these discoveries were, they were overshadowed, in 1865, when James Clerk Maxwell developed a set of mathematical equations which seemed to show that light, too, is electromagnetic—a stream of alternating electric and magnetic fields that covers a frequency spectrum only partly visible. This was unexpected and created a furor of excited controversy and doubt that did not subside until 1887 when Heinrich Hertz, in Germany, succeeded in generating the lower-frequency light waves Maxwell had predicted. We have since named them radio waves.

Thus, by 1887, we knew that electricity, magnetism, and light were all aspects of the same thing—electromagnetic energy. But light was not an electric current, magnets did not shock a person who touched them, and no one could see an electric field. What were the differences?

A solution to the puzzle began to take form ten years later with the discovery of the electron by Joseph Thomson, in England. Here, at last, was the source of Thales' amberous inhalations, Gray's electric currents, Franklin's negative charge, Galvani's salientian twitchings, Oersted's electromagnetism, and Faraday's chemical glue. Intensive studies of the new particle throughout the world have subsequently established that all matter contains electrons, that all electrons are identical, that they represent the smallest unit of negative electric charge, and that they all have the same mass (weight) and the same rate of spin. This last fact, incidentally, established that the electron is also the source of magnetism, since a moving electric charge creates a magnetic field at right angles to its motion or spin. But what was its connection with light and the newly found radio waves?

Since it was now clear that matter is made up of very tiny particles, was it not possible that light is also? Max Planck came close to saying so, in 1900, when he devised a formula which showed that electromagnetic energy trapped in a material cavity of uniform temperature can exist there only in certain precise amounts—*quanta,* he called them.

In 1905, following Planck's lead, Albert Einstein showed that this idea could also explain the photoelectric effect whereby certain materials emit electrons when exposed to light. A peculiarity of this emission is that the energy imparted to the electrons is a function not of the intensity of light but of its frequency, or color. This led Einstein to conclude that light is not an unbroken continuum of waves but a flow of indivisible "particles" of various energy "sizes." It is these, one or more of which is absorbed, in toto, by various electrons, that produce the photoemission effect. Such particles are now called *photons* and represent the minimum amount of electromagnetic energy that can exist at any one frequency.

Einstein went even further, in fact, and showed, with his special theory of relativity, that the mass of the electron and all other particles can itself be converted to pure electromagnetic energy, as occurs, to a large degree, in an atomic explosion. Thus, by 1905, the links between electricity, magnetism, and electromagnetism, or light, had finally been found.

Having discovered this brave new world of the electron, and having become acquainted with the character of its leading citizens, scientists now set out to investigate its geography and to study its environment, its domestic commerce, and its sociology. In short, they wanted to know how electrons "lived" in various materials, how forms of energy were traded back and forth among them, and what laws and codes governed their social intercourse in vacuum, plasma, gas, liquid, superfluid, and solid.

Lord Rutherford's discovery of the positively charged nucleus in 1911 and Niels Bohr's concept of the atomic solar system, with negatively charged electron planets orbiting a positively charged nuclear sun, announced in 1913, gave us an idea of how electron society is organized. But it was not until the invention of quantum mechanics, in the decade of the 1920s, that we could begin to understand electron sociology. We are still working at it, in fact.

Of course, we did not need all this understanding of internal electron society in order to start trading with it from outside. It was enough to know that certain electrons could be persuaded to leave their atomic homes, under certain conditions, and to work in metal or vacuum to produce all sorts of electromagnetic phenomena of use to man. Thus were the electric-power industry, the telephone industry, and the broadcasting and wireless communications industries founded, with all their supportive activities and services.

However, with the invention of the transistor in 1948, man demonstrated that he had, at last, learned to master the internal "politics" of electron society in solids and that he had learned to turn this knowledge to his advantage as well.

Seen in this perspective, electronics, since 1948, is a chronicle of the results produced by using quantum-mechanical principles and interpretations to explain electrical, magnetic, and electromagnetic phenomena in all its forms, especially those which obtain in the solid state. It is the application of quantum mechanics, coupled with man's great genius for invention, that has produced the transistor and semiconductor diode, the tunnel diode and Gunn effect oscillator, the electro-luminescent diode and laser, the hologram, and even the modern digital computer.

Digital computers are included because they are based on a theory that information can be made to consist of certain indivisible bits (quanta, if you will) that are best processed and communicated in just that form. In fact, it now appears that the next great area in electronics where the quantum *Weltanschauung* will be applied is in communications. There is a growing trend away from analog and toward digital communications, which means that all telephone conversations, radio broadcasts, and TV pictures may ultimately come to us in strings of tiny coded electromagnetic bursts that the ear and eye will reassemble into a familiar voice or a recognizable scene.

With the discovery of the electron and its significance, man ended a quest that began twenty-six centuries earlier in the speculations of Thales of Miletus. Moreover, as it turned out, man also reached the bottom of physical reality, insofar as he can know it directly. He can experience electronic phenomena as such, but nuclear phenomena can only be known indirectly by the effects they have upon the electrons that compose man or his instruments. Man is, each and every one, enveloped, in effect, by an electronic membrane that separates and, perhaps, protects him from nuclear reality. Not that that has stopped him. He has already deduced enough about nuclei to produce bombs, reactors, and radioactive tracers. But whether he finally succeeds in cornering the nucleus or not, for him, in the truest sense, the universe must be forever amberous.

Selected Bibliography

Chapter 1

Men Who Made a New Physics, Barbara Lovett Cline, New American Library, New York, 1969.

Elementary Solid State Physics, Charles Kittel, Wiley, New York, 1962.

Introduction to Solid State Physics, Charles Kittel, Wiley, New York, 1953.

A History of the Theories of Aether and Electricity, vol. 1 to 1900; vol. 2, 1900 to 1926, Nelson, New York, 1951, 1953.

The Rise of the New Physics, 2 vols., A. D'Abro, Dover, New York, 1939.

Chapter 2

Sources of Quantum Mechanics, Classics of Science, vol. 5, B. L. Van Der Waerden (ed.), Dover, New York, 1968.

Quantum Electronics, A. Yariv, Wiley, New York, 1968.

The Conceptual Development of Quantum Mechanics, M. Jammer, McGraw-Hill, New York, 1966.

Quantum Theory of Solids, Charles Kittel, Wiley, New York, 1963.
Quantum Mechanics, Leonard I. Schiff, McGraw-Hill, New York, 1955.

Chapter 3

Physics and Technology of Semiconductor Devices, Andrew S. Grove, Wiley, New York, 1967.
Parametric and Tunnel Diodes, Kern K. N. Chang, Prentice-Hall EE Series, W. L. Everitt (ed.), Prentice-Hall, Englewood Cliffs, N.J., 1964.
Compound Semiconductors, R. K. Willardson and H. L. Goering (eds.), vol. 1, *Preparation of III–V Compounds,* Reinhold, New York, 1962.
Transistor Physics and Circuits, Robert L. Riddle and Marlin P. Ristenblatt, Prentice-Hall, Englewood Cliffs, N.J., 1958.
Electrons and Holes in Semiconductors, W. Shockley, Van Nostrand, Princeton, N.J., 1953.

Chapter 4

"Crystal Growth, 1968," *Proceedings of the Second International Conference on Crystal Growth,* Birmingham, U.K., July 15–19, 1968, F. C. Frank, J. B. Mullin, H. S. Peiser (eds.), North-Holland Publishing Co., Amsterdam.
"Zone Refining," William G. Pfann, *Scientific American,* vol. 217, no. 6, pp. 62–72, December, 1967.
"Crystal Growth," *Proceedings of an International Conference on Crystal Growth,* Boston, June 20–24, 1966, Pergamon Press, New York.
The Art and Science of Growing Crystals, J. J. Gilman, Wiley, New York, 1963.
Preparation of Single Crystals, W. D. Lawson and S. Nielsen, Butterworth, London, 1958.
Growth and Perfection of Crystals, R. H. Doremus, B. W. Roberts, and D. Turnbull, Wiley, New York, 1958.
Zone Melting, W. G. Pfann, Wiley, New York, 1957.
Crystal Growth, H. E. Buckley, Wiley, New York, 1951.

Chapter 5

"Multielement Self-scanned Mosaic Sensors," P. Weimer, W. Pike, G. Sadasiv, F. V. Shallcross, and L. Meray-Horvath, *IEEE Spectrum,* pp. 52–65, March, 1969.
Photoemissive Materials, A. Sommer, Wiley, New York, 1968.

Physics of Thin Films, vol. 2, Hass and Thun (eds.), "The Insulated Gate Thin Film Transistor," P. Weimer, Academic, New York, 1964, pp. 147–192.

Advances in Electronics and Electron Physics, vol. 13, pp. 387–437, "TV Camera Tubes: A Research Review," Paul Weimer, Academic, New York, 1960.

Chapter 6

"The Si-SiO$_2$ Solid-State Interface System," A. G. Revesz and K. H. Zaininger, *RCA Review,* March, 1968.

"Field-Effect Transistors," *Physics: Technology and Applications,* Torkel Wallmark and Harwick H. Johnson, Prentice-Hall, Englewood Cliffs, N.J., 1966.

Semiconductor Surfaces, A. Many, Y. Goldstein, N. B. Grover, Wiley, New York, 1965.

Chapter 7

Scanning Electron Microscopy, P. A. Thornton, Chapman & Hall, London, 1968.

Quantitative Electron Probe Microanalysis, U.S. Dept. of Commerce, NBS, Special Publication 298, 1968.

Mass Spectrometry in Science and Technology, Frederick A. White, Wiley, New York, 1968.

The Electron Microscopy of Thin Crystals, by Hirsch, Howie, Nicholson, Pashley, and Whelan, Butterworth, London, 1965.

Spectrochemical Analysis, L. H. Ahrens and S. R. Taylor, Addison-Wesley, Reading, Mass., 1961.

X-ray Diffraction Procedures, Glug and Alexander, Wiley, New York, 1959.

Neutron Diffraction, G. E. Bacon, Clarendon Press, Oxford, 1955.

Electron Optics and the Electron Microscope, Zworykin, Morton, Hillier, and Vance, Wiley, New York, 1945.

Chapter 8

"Semiconductor Memory Circuits and Technology," Wendell B. Sanders, *Proceedings Fall Joint Computer Conference,* vol. 33, part 2, p. 1205, December, 1968.

"Silicon-on-sapphire Complementary MOS Memory Systems," J. R. Burns et al., *Digest of Technical Papers, ISSCC,* vol. 10, pp. 76–77, February, 1967.

"Taking Cryoelectric Memories Out of Cold Storage," Robert A. Gange, *Electronics Magazine,* vol. 40, no. 8, pp. 111–120, Apr. 17, 1967.

"Integrated Computer Memories," Jan A. Rajchman, *Scientific American,* vol. 217, no. 1, pp. 18–31, July, 1967.

Digital Computer Fundamentals, 2d ed., Thomas C. Bartee, McGraw-Hill, New York, 1966.

"Present and Future State-of-the-art in Computer Memories," L. C. Hobbs, *IEEE Transactions on Electronic Computers,* vol. EC-15, no. 4, pp. 534–550, August, 1966.

"Woven Wire Memory for NDRO System," H. Maeda et al., *IEEE Transactions on Electronic Computers,* vol. EC-15, no. 4, pp. 442–451, August, 1966.

"Memories in Present and Future Generations of Computers," *IEEE Spectrum,* November, 1965.

The Analytical Engine: Computers—Past, Present, and Future, Jeremy Bernstein, Random House, New York, 1963.

Square Loop Ferrite Circuitry: Storage and Logic Techniques, C. J. Quartly, Prentice-Hall, Englewood Cliffs, N.J., 1962.

"Digital Information Storage in Three Dimensions Using Magnetic Cores," J. W. Forrester, *Journal of Applied Physics,* vol. 22, pp. 44–48, 1951.

Chapter 9

"Artificial Intelligence: Themes in the Second Decade," E. Feigenbaum, *Proceedings of IFIP,* 1968 Conference, Spartan Books.

"Artificial Intelligence," Marvin Minsky, *Scientific American,* vol. 215, no. 3, September, 1966.

Computers and Thought, E. Feigenbaum and J. Feldman (eds.), McGraw-Hill, New York, 1963.

Chapter 10

Oxide Magnetic Materials, K. J. Standley, Clarendon Press, Oxford, 1962.

Ferrites, J. Smith and H. P. J. Wijn, Wiley, New York, 1959.

Chapter 11

"Transmission and Amplification of Acoustic Waves in Piezoelectric Semiconductors," J. H. McFee, in *Physics,* vol. 4, part A, Mason (ed.), Academic, New York, 1966.

"High-frequency Ultrasonic Stress Waves," Ron Truell and C. Elbaum, *Handbuch der Physik,* vol. xi–2, p. 246, 1962.

Acoustical Engineering, H. F. Olson, Van Nostrand, Princeton, N.J., 1957.

Chapter 12

Superconductivity, M. Tinkham, Gordon and Breach, New York, 1966.

Applied Superconductivity, Vernon L. Newhouse, Wiley, New York, 1964.

Superconductivity, E. A. Lynton, Wiley, New York, 1962.

Chapter 13

Plasmas in Solids, Solid State Physics, D. Turnbull, F. Seitz, and H. Ehrenreich (eds.), Academic, New York, 1970.

Plasma Effects in Solids, J. Bok (ed.), Dunod, Paris, 1965.

"Plasma Effects in Solids," *7th International Conference on the Physics of Semiconductors*, Dunod, Paris, 1964.

Physics of Fully Ionized Gases, 2d ed., Lyman Spitzer, Interscience Tracts on Physics and Astronomy, no. 3, Wiley, New York, 1962.

Chapter 14

"Review and Evaluation of Past Solar Cell Development Efforts," P. A. Crossley, Martin Wolf, and G. T. Noel, *final report on contract #NASW–1427*, RCA Astro Electronics Division, June, 1968.

Thermoelectric Power Supplies, Ye. K. Iordanishvili (machine transl. of original text), Moscow, 1968, FTD-MT-24-53-69; prepared by foreign technology division, Wright-Patterson Air Force Base, Dayton, Ohio.

Direct Energy Conversion, Stanley W. Angrist, Allyn and Bacon, Boston, 1965.

Thermoelectricity: Science and Engineering, Robert R. Heikes and Roland W. Ure, Jr., Interscience, New York, 1961.

Semiconductor Thermoelements and Thermoelectric Cooling, A. F. Ioffe, Infosearch Ltd., London, 1957.

Chapter 15

Microwave Semiconductor Devices and Their Circuit Applications, Hugh A. Watson (ed.), McGraw-Hill, New York, 1968.

Semiconductors and Semimetals, vol. 1, chap. by Betsy Ancker-Johnson, in R. C. Willardson and A. C. Beer (eds.), Academic, New York, 1966.

Microwave Solid-State Engineering, L. S. Nergaard and M. Glicksman, Van Nostrand, Princeton, N.J., 1965.

Chapter 16

Wave Interactions in Solid State Plasmas, Martin C. Steele and Bayrum Vural, McGraw-Hill, New York, May, 1969.

Waves in Anisotropic Plasmas, William P. Allis, Solomon J. Buchsbaum, Abraham Bers, M.I.T., Cambridge, Mass., 1963.

Proceedings of the Symposium on Millimeter Waves, Polytechnic Press, Polytechnic Institute, New York, 1959.

Chapter 17

Electrophotography, R. M. Schaffert, Focal Press, 1965.

Xerography and Related Processes, John H. Dessauer and Harold E. Clark (eds.), Focal Press, 1965.

Chapter 18

Optical Interactions in Solids, B. di Bartolo, Wiley, New York, 1967.

Optical Physics, Max Garbuny, Academic, New York, 1965.

Photoelectronic Materials and Devices, S. Larach (ed.), Van Nostrand, Princeton, N.J., 1965.

A History of Luminescence: From the Earliest Times until 1900, American Philosophical Society, Philadelphia, 1957.

Chapter 19

Gas Lasers, Arnold L. Bloom, Wiley, New York, 1968.

Laser Systems and Applications, Herbert A. Elion, Pergamon Press, New York, 1967.

Gas Lasers, Charles G. B. Garrett, McGraw-Hill, New York, 1967.

Introduction to Laser Physics, Bela A. Lengyel, Wiley, New York, 1966.

Lasers and Their Applications, Kurt R. Stehling, World Publishing, Cleveland, 1966.

The Laser, Smith and Sorokin, McGraw-Hill, New York, 1966.

Applied Optics, Optical Society of America, 1965.

Masers and Lasers: How They Work, What They Do, Manfred Brotherton, McGraw-Hill, New York, 1965.

Chapter 20

"A New Electric Field Controlled Reflective Optical Storage Effect in Mixed Liquid Crystal Systems," G. Heilmeier, *IEEE Proceedings,* vol. 56, p. 34, January, 1969.

"Reflective Liquid Crystal Television Display," John van Raalte, *IEEE Proceedings*, vol. 56, p. 2146, December, 1968.

"Dynamic Scattering in Liquid Crystals," G. Heilmeier, *Appliance Engineer*, vol. 2, no. 4, p. 21, November, 1968.

"Dynamic Scattering: A New Electro-optical Effect in Certain Classes of Nematic Liquid Crystals," George Heilmeier, *IEEE Proceedings*, vol. 56, p. 1162, July, 1968.

"Photo-erasable Dark Trace Cathode Ray Storage Tube," W. Phillips and Z. J. Kiss, *IEEE Proceedings*, vol. 56, no. 11, pp. 2072–2073, 1968.

"Photoinduced Reversible Charge Transfer of Electrons in Transition Metal Doped $SrTiO_3$," B. W. Faughnan and Z. J. Kiss, *Physical Review Letters*, vol. 21, no. 18, pp. 1331–1334, 1968.

Physics of Color Centers, W. Beall Fowler (ed.), Academic, New York, 1968.

"Electron Spin Resonance Investigation of Photochromic Sodalities," H. G. Hodgson, J. S. Brinnen, and E. F. Williams, *Journal of Chemical Physics*, vol. 47, p. 3719, 1967.

"Liquid Crystals," J. A. Fergason, *Scientific American*, vol. 211, p. 77, 1964.

Molecular Structure and the Properties of Liquid Crystals, Gray, Academic, New York, 1962.

Television in Science and Industry, V. Zworykin, E. Ramberg, L. Flory, Wiley, New York, 1958.

Chapter 21

Lasers: Tools of Modern Technology, Ronald Brown, Doubleday Science Series, Doubleday, Garden City, N.Y., 1968.

An Introduction to Coherent Optics and Holography, George W. Stroke, Academic, New York, 1966.

Chapter 22

A History of Electricity, Edward Tatnall Canby, Hawthorn, New York, 1963.

Name Index

Name Index

Subject Index

Subject Index